S0-BER-023

AYP Monitoring Assessments provides a clear path to *adequate yearly progress* through systematic testing and recommendations for remediation. Progress monitoring at regular intervals ensures that students understand key content before moving on in the course. With the results of these tests, you will know when to modify instruction because a class is having difficulty and when to assign remediation because individual students need more help.

Beginning the Year: Establishing the Baseline

Teaching for adequate yearly progress (AYP) begins with evaluating student strengths and weaknesses. Before launching into the curriculum, you need to know how well your students read and how proficient they are in social studies skills. Use the following tests to measure student readiness for your course.

Screening Tests (pages 5–16)

Administer the Screening Tests to evaluate students' ability to read the textbook. These tests identify students who are reading two or more years below grade level. You may wish to consider placing them in intensive intervention. For students with lesser difficulties, you can use the recommendations for Differentiated Instruction in the Teacher's Edition of your textbook.

Diagnosing Readiness Tests (pages 17–62)

The Diagnosing Readiness Tests measure your students' abilities in skills essential to success in social studies. There is one test in each of the following categories:

- Geographic Literacy
- Visual Analysis
- Critical Thinking and Reading
- Communications
- Vocabulary
- Writing

Once you have test results, consult the correlation table in this book to locate program resources for instruction and practice in individual skills. Repeat these tests as least once more during the year to gauge student progress and identify skills needing improvement.

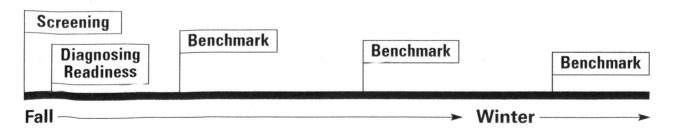

Monitoring Progress Over the Year

The section and chapter assessments in the Student Edition and Teaching Resources measure understanding of what students have learned on a short-term basis. To measure student retention over time, it is important to administer benchmark tests and refocus instruction based on test results.

Benchmark Tests (pages 71–93)

Benchmark testing is at the heart of progress monitoring and student achievement. At specified intervals throughout the year, give Benchmark Tests to evaluate student progress toward mastery of essential content. All questions on the Benchmark Tests correlate to core standards established for this course. See standards on page 70.

Critical to student achievement is analyzing benchmark tests results to adapt your teaching to student needs. Item tallies will show you areas where the whole class is having difficulty and thus merit reteaching. Items with just a few incorrect answers indicate that only certain students need remediation assignments.

Report Sheets (pages 94–99)

The student Benchmark Test report sheet identifies

- test items by number
- correlated standards
- student performance on each test item
- relevant assignments in the *Reading and Vocabulary Study Guide* for remediation of items that students have missed

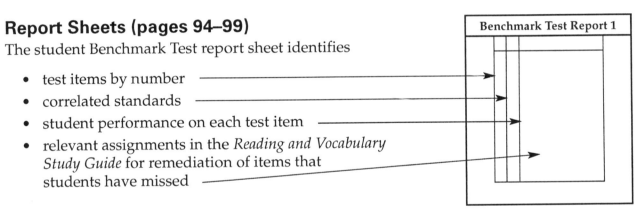

Benchmark Test Report 1

Ending the Year

Modifying your teaching as indicated by the results of the Screening, Diagnosing Readiness, and Benchmark tests throughout the school year sets the stage for your students to achieve adequate yearly progress.

Outcome Test (pages 100–104)

Administer the Outcome Test to see how well students have mastered course content. Like the Benchmark Tests, Outcome Test items are correlated to course standards.

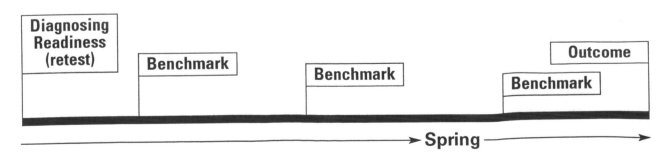

Civics

★ Government and Economics in Action ★

AYP Monitoring Assessments

PEARSON

Boston, Massachusetts
Glenview, Illinois
Parsippany, New Jersey
Shoreview, Minnesota
Upper Saddle River, New Jersey

13-digit ISBN 978-0-13-365183-6
10-digit ISBN 0-13-365183-5

Prentice Hall® and **Pearson Prentice Hall**™ are trademarks, in the U.S. and/or in other countries, of Pearson Education, Inc., or its affiliate(s).

2 3 4 5 6 7 8 9 10   11 10 09

Table of Contents

Screening Tests

Middle Grades, Test 1

Directions: *Read each passage. Then read each question that follows the passage. Decide which is the best answer to each question. Mark the letter for that answer.*

from Papa's Parrot
by Cynthia Rylant

Though his father was fat and merely owned a candy and nut shop, Harry Tillian liked his papa. Harry stopped liking candy and nuts when he was around seven, but, in spite of this, he and Mr. Tillian had remained friends and were still friends the year Harry turned twelve.

For years, after school, Harry had always stopped in to see his father at work. Many of Harry's friends stopped there, too, to spend a few cents choosing penny candy from the giant bins or to sample Mr. Tillian's latest batch of roasted peanuts. Mr. Tillian looked forward to seeing his son and his son's friends every day. He liked the company.

When Harry entered junior high school, though, he didn't come by the candy and nut shop as often. Nor did his friends. They were older and they had more spending money. They went to a burger place. They played video games. They shopped for records. None of them were much interested in candy and nuts anymore.

A new group of children came to Mr. Tillian's shop now. But not Harry Tillian and his friends.

The year Harry turned twelve was also the year Mr. Tillian got a parrot. He went to a pet store one day and bought one for more money than he could really afford. He brought the parrot to his shop, set its cage near the sign for maple clusters, and named it Rocky.

Harry thought this was the strangest thing his father had ever done, and he told him so, but Mr. Tillian just ignored him.

Rocky was good company for Mr. Tillian. When business was slow, Mr. Tillian would turn on a small color television he had sitting in a corner, and he and Rocky would watch the soap operas. Rocky liked to scream when the romantic music came on, and Mr. Tillian would yell at him to shut up, but they seemed to enjoy themselves.

The more Mr. Tillian grew to like his parrot, and the more he talked to it instead of to people, the more embarrassed Harry became. Harry would stroll past the shop, on his way somewhere else, and he'd take a quick look inside to see what his dad was doing. Mr. Tillian was always talking to the bird. So Harry kept walking.

At home things were different. Harry and his father joked with each other at the dinner table as they always had—Mr. Tillian teasing Harry about his smelly socks; Harry teasing Mr. Tillian about his blubbery stomach. At home things seemed all right.

1. **The author of this story gives you enough information to believe that Mr. Tillian**
   A. enjoys Harry's company.
   B. is embarrassed by his son.
   C. is angry with Harry.
   D. prefers children to teenagers.

2. **The word romantic in this story means**
   A. sentimental.
   B. funny.
   C. foolish.
   D. critical.

3. **The main point of the story is that**
   A. people outgrow their interest in candy and nuts.
   B. parrots can serve as replacements for children.
   C. children and parents often become bitter enemies as children grow older.
   D. behavior between parents and children can change as children grow older.

4. **Which of these sentences expresses a FACT from the story?**
   A. Rocky does not like romantic music.
   B. Rocky cost a lot of money.
   C. Mr. Tillian sells maple clusters at his store.
   D. Harry eats cheeseburgers and fries.

5. **Which of these best explains why Mr. Tillian buys Rocky?**
   A. Rocky can be trained to talk.
   B. Mr. Tillian wants to tease Harry.
   C. Parrots like nuts.
   D. Mr. Tillian is lonely.

6. **The year Harry turns twelve is significant because**
   A. he and his friends play video games and shop for records.
   B. he finds interests outside the candy store.
   C. Mr. Tillian watches soap operas.
   D. a new group of children comes to the store.

Middle Grades, Test 2

from Pandas
by Gillian Standring

The giant panda is one of the best-known animals in the world. It is also one of the rarest. In 1990 there were only about one thousand giant pandas living wild in China, and only fifteen in zoos outside China. So if you have seen pandas in a zoo, you are very lucky.

Pandas, unlike people, prefer to be cool and damp. Hot, dry weather is bad for them. High up in the mountains of Sichuan in southwest China, there are thick, misty forests where it is always cool and damp. Pandas spend most of the year in these forests. In winter they come down to the lower slopes to get away from the deep snow and freezing cold.

Pandas are famous for eating bamboo. Their food grows all around them in the bamboo forests, so they never have to hunt for it. However, they like to eat only a few kinds of bamboo, and their digestion is not very good, so they spend almost all the day just eating. Pandas also eat grasses, roots, bulbs, and tree bark. Sometimes they catch little cane rats and fish. They often take long drinks from mountain streams and rivers.

Giant pandas have probably never been common anywhere. There are several reasons for this. They do not produce many babies. As we have seen, they can live only in cool bamboo forests. Each panda needs a big area of forest to itself, and even large areas of suitable mountain forest have room for only a few pandas.

For thousands of years, the giant panda's homeland in southwest China was very hard for people to reach, so it was left undisturbed for pandas and other wildlife. Now the millions of Chinese people need more land for their farms and villages. Modern roads help them to reach even the farthest mountains of Sichuan. As the people cut down the mountain forests, the pandas have fewer unspoiled bamboo grooves to live in.

There is some good news for pandas, however. The Chinese people and international conservation organizations are working hard to protect them. Now there are thirteen special panda reserves in China, where some 800 pandas are living in safety. The reserves were created to protect the pandas and the bamboo forests they need. The cutting down of bamboo and felling of trees by people is strictly controlled.

If we can give enough support to the efforts to save pandas, perhaps in the next century there will be more pandas in the world than now.

7. **What is this passage mostly about?**
   A. the lifecycle of the giant panda
   B. information about giant pandas
   C. animals of the bamboo forest
   D. panda reserves in China

8. **You can tell from the passage that the areas where giant pandas live are limited because**
   A. the writer says so.
   B. giant pandas are rare.
   C. they can only live in cool bamboo forests in China.
   D. few giant pandas live in zoos outside China.

9. **Which of these is an OPINION in the passage?**
   A. Giant pandas prefer to be cool and damp.
   B. There are thirteen panda reserves in China.
   C. The giant panda's homeland used to be hard to reach.
   D. You are lucky if you have seen pandas in a zoo.

10. **Which of these is a FACT in the passage?**
    A. There are not enough giant pandas in the world.
    B. Giant pandas eat mostly cane rats and fish.
    C. If we help giant pandas now, there will be more in the future.
    D. Each giant panda needs a large area of forest to itself.

11. **You can tell that the author of this passage believes that**
    A. people in China should not build so many roads.
    B. giant pandas should have to hunt for their food.
    C. the mountains of Sichuan have a pleasant climate.
    D. giant pandas and bamboo forests need to be protected.

12. **The word reserves in this passage means**
    A. farms.
    B. national parks.
    C. sets aside.
    D. areas of land set apart.

13. **There is enough information in this passage to show that**
    A. zoos outside of China help giant pandas.
    B. the giant panda population is dying off rapidly.
    C. the giant panda's habitat is being threatened.
    D. for thousands of years, there were no farms in China.

14. **According to this passage, the panda reserves allow conservationists to**
    A. count how many giant pandas live in the wild.
    B. find out how much bamboo each panda eats.
    C. control the impact people have on the giant panda's habitat
    D. keep track of new panda babies.

Middle Grades, Test 3

from Into Thin Air
by Jon Krakauer

If the Icefall required few orthodox climbing techniques, it demanded a whole new repertoire of skills in their stead—for instance, the ability to tiptoe in mountaineering boots and crampons across three wobbly ladders lashed end to end, bridging a sphincter-clenching chasm. There were many such crossings, and I never got used to them.

At one point I was balanced on an unsteady ladder in the predawn gloaming, stepping tenuously from one bent rung to the next, when the ice supporting the ladder on either end began to quiver as if an earthquake had struck. A moment later came an explosive roar as a large serac somewhere close above came crashing down. I froze, my heart in my throat, but the avalanching ice passed fifty yards to the left, out of sight, without doing any damage. After waiting a few minutes to regain my composure I resumed my herky-jerky passage to the far side of the ladder.

The glacier's continual and often violent state of flux added an element of uncertainty to every ladder crossing. As the glacier moved, crevasses would sometimes compress, buckling ladders like toothpicks; other times a crevasse might expand, leaving a ladder dangling in the air, only tenuously supported, with neither end mounted on solid ice. Anchors securing the ladders and lines routinely melted out when the afternoon sun warmed the surrounding ice and snow. Despite daily maintenance, there was a very real danger that any given rope might pull loose under body weight.

But if the Icefall was strenuous and terrifying, it had a surprising allure as well. As dawn washed the darkness from the sky, the shattered glacier was revealed to be a three-dimensional landscape of phantasmal beauty. The temperature was six degrees Fahrenheit. My crampons crunched reassuringly into the glacier's rind. Following the fixed line, I meandered through a vertical maze of crystalline blue stalagmites. Sheer rock buttresses seamed with ice pressed in from both edges of the glacier, rising like the shoulders of a malevolent god. Absorbed by my surroundings and the gravity of the labor, I lost myself in the unfettered pleasures of ascent, and for an hour or two actually forgot to be afraid.

15. **You can tell from the passage that the word serac means**
   A. a summit of a mountain.
   B. a hole in the ice.
   C. a mass of ice.
   D. a volcanic peak of a mountain.

16. **You can tell from the context that the word crevasses means**
   A. avalanches.
   B. safety ropes.
   C. cracks in a glacier.
   D. freezing and melting water.

17. **The author's emotions can best be identified as**
   A. excitement and fear.
   B. confidence and joy.
   C. relaxation and delight.
   D. nervousness and depression.

18. **Based on the passage, you can tell that the author thought the climb was**
   A. effortless.
   B. terrifying.
   C. exhausting.
   D. impossible.

19. **You can tell from the passage that sunlight made the glacier**
   A. safer to navigate.
   B. more dangerous and beautiful.
   C. harder to look at directly.
   D. larger and steeper.

20. **The author never got over his fear of**
   A. early morning climbing.
   B. crossing ladder bridges.
   C. blue stalagmites.
   D. rock buttresses.

21. **The passage gives you reason to believe that**
   A. mountain climbing can be a life-threatening sport.
   B. the author should have trained harder.
   C. the author thought mainly about returning unharmed.
   D. mountain climbing is a good activity for reducing stress.

22. **Which of these sentences expresses a FACT from the passage?**
   A. The glacier is in a constant state of change.
   B. The bridges needed to be better maintained.
   C. The author realized his dream of conquering Mount Everest.
   D. No one ever gets used to crossing the Icefall.

23. **Based on the passage, you can conclude that**
   A. the author's climb is going to be his last.
   B. the Icefall presents unusual challenges to mountain climbers.
   C. frostbite is a very real danger of mountain climbing.
   D. the members of a mountain-climbing expedition are dependent on each other.

24. **What is this passage mostly about?**
   A. surviving an avalanche
   B. climbing techniques
   C. climbing a glacier
   D. crossing a crevasse

Screening Tests

High School, Test 1

Directions: *Read each passage. Then read each question that follows the passage. Decide which is the best answer to each question. Mark the letter for that answer.*

from In Patagonia by Bruce Chatwin

He was a nice boy, a lively friendly-faced boy, who loved his Mormon family and the cabin in the cottonwoods. Both his parents came out from England as children and trekked the Plains, with Brigham Young's handcart companies, from Iowa City to the Salt Lake. Anne Parker was a nervous and highly strung Scotswoman; her husband, Max, a simple soul, who had a hard time squeezing a living from the homestead and made a little extra in timber haulage.

The two-room cabin is still standing at Circleville, Utah. The corrals are there, and the paddock where Robert Leroy rode his first calf. The poplars he planted still line the irrigation ditch between the orchard and the sage. He was the oldest of eleven children, a boy of precise loyalties and a sense of fair play. He dreamed of being a cowboy and, in dime novels, read the on-going saga of Jesse James.

At eighteen he identified as his natural enemies the cattle companies, the railroads and the banks, and convinced himself that right lay [on] the wrong side of the law. One June morning in 1884, awkwardly and ashamed, he told his mother he was going to work in a mine at Telluride. She gave him her father's blue traveling blanket and a pot of blueberry preserves. He kissed his baby sister, Lula, crying in her cradle, and rode out of their lives. The truth came out when Max Parker returned to the homestead. His son had rustled some cattle with a young outlaw called Mike Cassidy. The law was after them both.

Bob Parker took the name Cassidy and rode into a new life of wide horizons and the scent of horse leather. (Butch was the name of a borrowed gun.) His apprentice years, the 1880's, were years of the Beef Bonanza; of Texas longhorns peppering the range; of the Cattle Barons who paid miserly wages and dividends of 40 per cent to their shareholders; of champagne breakfasts at the Cheyenne Club and the English dukes who called their cowboys "cow-servants" and whose cowboys called them "dudes." There were plenty of Englishmen knocking round the West: one cowboy wrote to his Yankee employer: "That Inglishman yu lef in charge at the other ranch got to fresh and we had to kil him. Nothing much has hapened since yu lef . . ."

Then the great white winter of 1886–7 wiped out three-quarters of the stock. Greed combined with natural catastrophe to breed a new type, the cowboy-outlaw, men driven by unemployment and black-listing into criminal hideouts and the rustling game. At Brown's Hole or Hole-in-the-Wall they joined up with professional desperadoes; men like Black Jack Ketchum, or the psychopath Harry Tracy, or Flat-Nose George Curry, or Harvey Logan, the diarist of his own murders.

Butch Cassidy, in those years, was drover, horse-wrangler, mavericker, part-time bank-robber, and leader of men; the sheriffs feared him most for the last of these accomplishments. In 1894 they gave him two years in the Wyoming State Penitentiary for stealing a horse he hadn't stolen, valued at five dollars. The sentence soured him to any further dealing with the law. And, from 1896 to 1901, his Train Robbers'

Syndicate, better known as The Wild Bunch, performed the string of perfect hold-ups that kept lawmen, Pinkerton detectives and the railroad in perpetual jitters. The stories of his antics are endless; breathless rides along the Outlaw Trail; shooting glass conductors from telegraph poles; or paying a poor widow's rent by robbing the rent man. The homesteaders loved him. Many were Mormons, outlawed themselves for polygamy. They gave him food, shelter, alibis, and occasionally their daughters. Today, he would be classed as a revolutionary. But he had no sense of political organization.

Butch Cassidy never killed a man. Yet his friends were seasoned killers; their murders drove him to fits of remorse. He hated having to rely on the deadly aim of Harry Longabaugh, the Pennsylvania German with evil blue eyes and a foul temper. He tried to go straight, but there was too much on his Pinkerton card and his pleas for amnesty went unheard. Each new robbery spawned another and added years to his sentence.

1. **Which of these is the best summary of the passage?**
   A. Butch Cassidy decided to become an outlaw at an early age.
   B. Butch Cassidy became a bank robber out of necessity.
   C. Butch Cassidy became an outlaw after he was falsely accused of stealing a horse.
   D. Butch Cassidy technically was an outlaw, but he felt like he was doing the right thing.

2. **What is the first paragraph of this passage mainly about?**
   A. Cassidy's father had a hard time making a living.
   B. The Mormons trekked to the Salt Lake.
   C. Cassidy came from a good family.
   D. Cassidy's mother made him nervous.

3. **The author says that today Cassidy "would be classed as a revolutionary" because**
   A. he fought in the Revolutionary War.
   B. he rebelled against a system that was often unfair and unpopular.
   C. he was a good leader and a moving public speaker.
   D. his actions fundamentally changed the lives of people living in the American West.

4. **Butch Cassidy left home when he was eighteen and**
   A. rustled cattle.
   B. went to work at a mine in Telluride.
   C. killed a man.
   D. tried to get a homestead of his own.

5. **From the information in the passage, you can conclude that Butch Cassidy was**
   A. tortured by the murders he committed.
   B. a bad man.
   C. the perfect outlaw.
   D. a complicated man.

6. **The author includes the last paragraph of the passage in order to**
   A. show how bloodthirsty Cassidy's friends were.
   B. explain why Cassidy remained an outlaw.
   C. show how unhappy Cassidy was with his life.
   D. explain why operating costs were so high.

Name_____ Class_____ Date _____

High School, Test 2

from Joy, Luck and Hollywood
by Amy Tan
Los Angeles Times, Calendar magazine, September 5, 1993

What's it like watching your first novel become a movie? For Amy Tan, it was as unlikely an experience as *The Joy Luck Club* was an unlikely bestseller. The book, the interwoven stories of four Chinese-American mothers and their contemporary-minded daughters, has sold more than 275,000 copies in hardcover and had 33 printings in paperback since it was first published in 1989. And Wednesday, the $10.6 million Hollywood Pictures production of Tan's novel, written by Tan and Ron Bass and directed by Wayne Wang, opens here and in New York. Calendar asked Tan, 41, to write about her experiences dealing with Hollywood, from her initial feelings about the movies to her first look at the finished film.

. . . I saw all the dailies, most of them on video format at home. I cried throughout the making of the movie. I was very moved by what I was seeing. I was exhausted watching what the actors went through. At major stages, Ron and I worked with Wayne and the editor, Maysie Hoy, as the movie was being cut. That process was fascinating but tedious. I ended up thinking Maysie was a saint.

Around April, I got to see a first rough cut. I was supposed to watch it and take notes of problem areas and such. But I was too mesmerized to do anything but watch it pretty much like an ordinary moviegoer. I laughed, I cried. The second time I saw it, I said to Wayne: "I want you to remember this day. We're going to get a lot of different reactions to this film later down the road. But I want us to remember that on this day, you, Ron and I were proud with what we've accomplished. We made our vision."

Ron insisted that I come to the test previews because there I'd get some of the biggest highs or lows of my life, seeing how a real audience reacted. Fortunately, it was the former. I was surprised, though, whenever people laughed during a scene I never considered funny. I suppose it was one of those ironic laughs, in which one recognizes the pain of some childhood humiliation.

I've now seen the movie about 25 times, and I am not ashamed to say I'm moved to tears each time.

By the time you read this, I will have seen the movie with my mother and my half sister, who just immigrated from China. So that'll be my version of life imitating art, or sitting in front of it. I'm nervous about what my mother will think. I'm afraid she'll be overwhelmed by some of the scenes that are taken from her life, especially the one that depicts the suicide of her mother.

I hope those in the audience are moved by the film, that they connect with the emotions and feel changed at the end, that they feel closer to another person as a result. That's what I like to get out of a book, a connection with the world.

As to reviews, I've already imagined all the bad things that can be said. That way I'll be delighted by anything good that comes out. I'm aware that the success of this movie will depend on good reviews and word-of-mouth reactions. But there comes a point when you've done all you can. And then it's out of your control. Certainly I hope the movie's a success at the box office, mostly for Wayne and Ron's sakes, as well as the cast and crew who worked on this. And certainly I hope

Disney feels that it was more than justified in taking a risk on this movie. By my score, however, the movie is already a success. We made the movie we wanted to make. It's not perfect, but we're happy with it. And I'll be standing in line, ready to plunk down $7 to see it.

In the meantime, I've got a whole mess of Chinese lucky charms that are absolutely guaranteed to bring the gods to the theater.

At different points in the making of the movie, I vowed I'd never do this again. It's too time-consuming. It's rife with ups and downs. There's so much business. I've developed some calluses and a certain sang-froid attitude about some of the inherent difficulties of filmmaking.

Yet, against all my expectations, I like working collaboratively from time to time, I like fusing ideas into one vision. I like seeing that vision come to life with other people who know exactly what it took to get there.

My love of fiction is unaltered. It's my first love. But, yes, I'll make another film with Ron and Wayne. It'll probably be my second novel, *The Kitchen God's Wife*. We've already started breaking the scenes out with page counts and narrative text. We started the day after we saw the first rough cut of *The Joy Luck Club*.

7. **According to the passage, author was surprised when people watching the movie**
   A. cried during some funny scenes.
   B. were moved by the film.
   C. laughed during a scene she didn't think was funny.
   D. felt changed at the end of the film.

8. **When the author mentions "the former" in the middle of paragraph 4, she is referring to**
   A. the first test preview.
   B. the last book she wrote.
   C. some of the biggest lows of her life.
   D. some of the biggest highs of her life.

9. **The author probably includes details about what she said to the movie's director after she saw the movie the second time because she wants to show**
   A. how proud of the film they were on that day.
   B. how upset about the film she was on that day.
   C. how difficult it was to work with the director.
   D. that she and the director had a good relationship.

10. **The main idea of this passage is that Amy Tan**
    A. is happy with the movie version of her book.
    B. found making her book into a movie to be exhausting.
    C. wants to make another movie.
    D. had difficulty working with other people to make the movie.

11. **Based on this passage, you can conclude that the author's mother**
    A. had some difficult times in China.
    B. was overwhelmed by her daughter's movie.
    C. still lives in China.
    D. was excited to see her daughter's movie.

Name_____ Class _____ Date _____

Baseball: National and International

When "Casey at the Bat" first appeared, baseball was rapidly becoming the national pastime of the United States. The game probably evolved from the game of rounders, which also involved hitting a ball with a bat. In rounders, however, a fielder put a runner out by actually hitting him with the ball.

English colonists brought rounders with them to the American colonies in the 1700s. By the mid-nineteenth century, rounders had become baseball, largely through the efforts of the sportsman Alexander Cartwright. In 1845, he founded the first organized baseball club—the Knickerbocker Base Ball Club of New York. He also set down the first rules for the game.

In 1846 the first official baseball game was played in Hoboken, New Jersey, by Cartwright's team and the New York Nine. The man who wrote the rulebook had the unpleasant experience of seeing his team lose, 23 to 1!

The Civil War made the game a national diversion. Confederate prisoners watched with fascination as Union soldiers from the Northeast played baseball in camp. After the war, soldiers from other parts of the country brought the game home with them.

In 1869 the Cincinnati Red Stockings became the first truly professional ball team with every team member paid for his efforts. For the next fifty years, baseball was played somewhat differently from the way it is today because the ball was heavier and had less bounce. Unable to hit the ball long distances, batters tried to place it strategically. Base stealing and <u>bunting</u> were therefore more common than they are today.

Given the importance of base running, it is not surprising that the real-life player who rivaled the fictional Casey (of "Casey at the Bat") in popularity was a champion base runner, King Kelly. Fans of the late 1800s cheered him on to home plate with cries of "Slide, Kelly, slide!"

Banned from playing professional baseball with white players, black players established their own teams as early as the 1880s. By 1920 they had organized their own national league. In the early days, players slept in second-rate motels and played in rundown stadiums. Soon, however, Negro league players enjoyed celebrity status in the black community. As the leagues' popularity grew, teams were able to afford their own stadiums and travel the country in luxurious Pullman train cars.

Major league baseball was finally integrated in 1947 when Jackie Robinson signed with the Brooklyn Dodgers. This opened the door for other talented black ballplayers, and brought to a close an important chapter in the history of baseball in the United States.

Today, baseball is played around the world. It is a major sport in Puerto Rico, home of the legendary baseball player Roberto Clemente, as well as in the Dominican Republic and Cuba. It is also popular in Italy, Canada, the Netherlands, and South Africa.

In Japan, baseball is as popular as sumo wrestling. Japanese teams have even hired seasoned American ballplayers to improve the performance of their home-grown players.

12. **From the 1870s to the 1920s baseball was played differently from the way it is played today because**
   A. the ball was different.
   B. people were not paid to play.
   C. Americans were still playing a form of rounders.
   D. the Cincinnati Red Stockings changed the rules.

13. **In the passage the word <u>bunting</u> most nearly means**
   A. a small, stout-billed bird.
   B. a thin fabric used in flags.
   C. tapping a ball without swinging the bat.
   D. staying at second-rate hotels.

14. **Baseball probably evolved from rounders because in that game**
   A. hitters "rounded" bases just as they do in baseball.
   B. fielders put a runner out by hitting him with a ball.
   C. speed and accuracy were also important.
   D. players hit a ball with a bat.

15. **Alexander Cartwright might have been disappointed by**
   A. baseball becoming a professional sport.
   B. losing the first official baseball game.
   C. organizing the Knickerbocker Base Ball Club of New York.
   D. writing the rulebook for baseball.

16. **According to this passage, the event that integrated baseball was**
   A. Roberto Clemente's arrival from Puerto Rico.
   B. African Americans starting their own national league.
   C. Jackie Robinson's signing with the Brooklyn Dodgers.
   D. African Americans touring the country playing baseball.

17. **Which of these is the best summary of this passage?**
   A. Base running is important in baseball.
   B. Baseball has evolved over the years and become a popular sport.
   C. Many countries around the world are playing baseball.
   D. Baseball is the most important contribution of the American colonists.

Name_____ Class_____ Date _____

Diagnosing Readiness Tests

Middle Grades Test 1 — Geographic Literacy

Directions: *Use the diagram below to answer questions 1–4.*

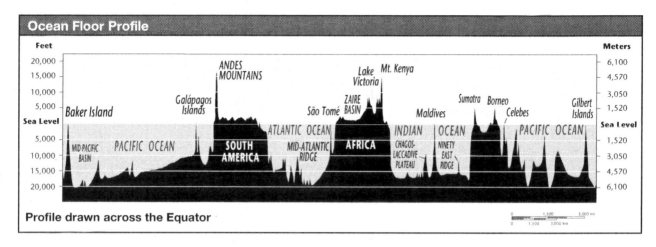

1. **What area of the world is shown on this map?**
   A. the ocean floor below South America and Africa
   B. the ocean floor below all of Earth
   C. the ocean floor along the Equator
   D. the ocean floor along the Eastern Hemisphere of Earth

2. **According to this diagram, what do Baker Island, the Galápagos Islands, and the Maldives have in common?**
   A. They are below sea level.
   B. They are at sea level.
   C. They are in the Pacific Ocean.
   D. They are surrounded by land.

3. **On this profile of the ocean floor, where are the lowest points on Earth located?**
   A. on the coast of Africa
   B. in the Indian Ocean
   C. on the coast of South America
   D. in the Atlantic Ocean

4. **Based on the information in the diagram, which of the following is a true statement?**
   A. Mt. Kenya is the highest point on the South American continent.
   B. Celebes and Borneo are higher than Sumatra.
   C. Most of South America is at or near sea level at the equator, and most of Africa is above sea level at the equator.
   D. Lake Victoria is located at sea level.

Middle Grades Test 1 — Geographic Literacy *(continued)*

Directions: *Use the diagram below to answer questions 5–9.*

5. According to this map, what area of Africa generally has the fewest people per square mile?

   A. central

   B. north

   C. south

   D. southwest

6. About how many people live in the city of Cairo, Egypt?

   A. between 2,000,000 and 4,999,999

   B. less than 1 person per square mile

   C. between 5,000,000 and 9,999,999

   D. 10,000,000 or more

7. What is the approximate distance between Cape Town, South Africa, and Harare, Zimbabwe?

   A. about 1,400 miles

   B. about 1,000 miles

   C. about 1,200 miles

   D. about 2,000 miles

8. Which of the following cities has the highest population?

   A. Tripoli, Libya

   B. Alexandria, Egypt

   C. Cairo, Egypt

   D. Dar es Salaam, Tanzania

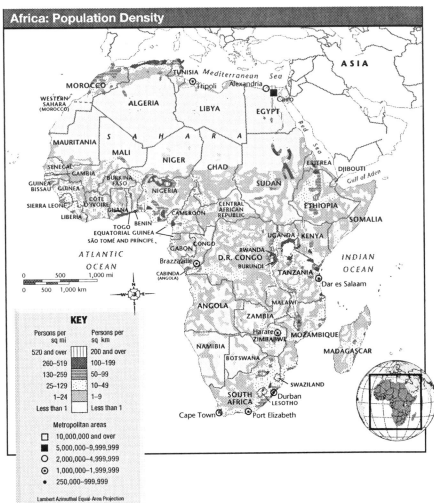

9. Using this map, what is one thing the South African cities of Cape Town, Port Elizabeth, and Durban have in common?

   A. They are in areas with 10 to 49 people per square mile.

   B. They are located on Africa's western coast.

   C. They are located on Africa's southern coast.

   D. Their populations are 10,000,000 and over.

Middle Grades Test 1 — Geographic Literacy (continued)

Directions: *Use the diagram below to answer questions 10–13.*

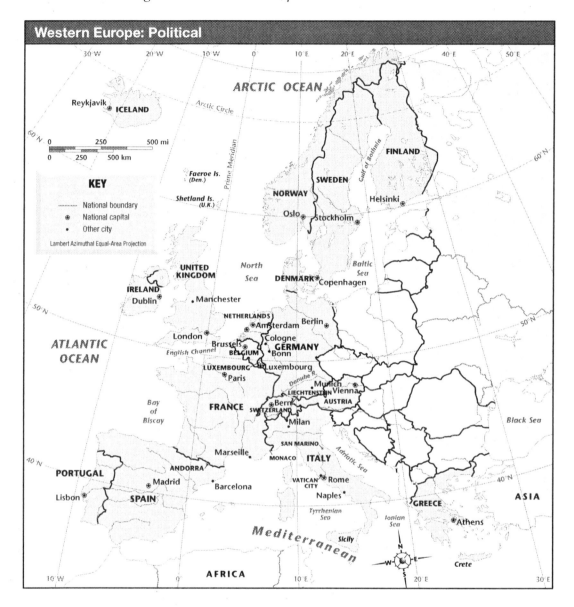

10. **What is the capital city of Italy?**
    A. Rome
    B. Milan
    C. Naples
    D. Paris

11. **Which of the following cities is the closest in distance to Vienna, Austria?**
    A. Lisbon
    B. Helsinki
    C. Athens
    D. Dublin

12. **Which country is located west of Spain?**
    A. Portugal
    B. United Kingdom
    C. Finland
    D. Italy

13. **Which body of water separates the United Kingdom and France?**
    A. Bay of Biscay
    B. English Channel
    C. North Sea
    D. Mediterranean Sea

Middle Grades Test 1 — Geographic Literacy (continued)

Directions: *Use the diagram below to answer questions 14–17.*

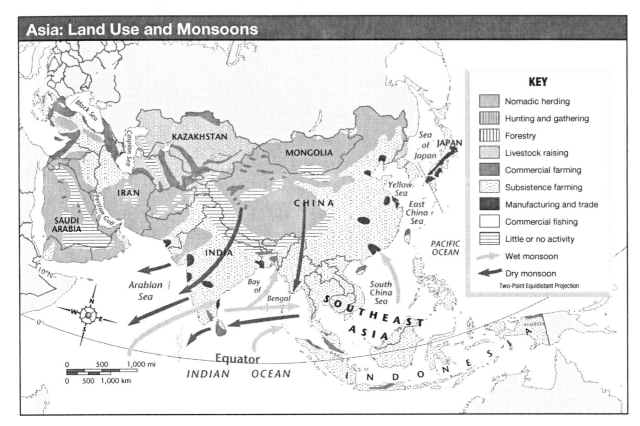

Asia: Land Use and Monsoons

KEY
- Nomadic herding
- Hunting and gathering
- Forestry
- Livestock raising
- Commercial farming
- Subsistence farming
- Manufacturing and trade
- Commercial fishing
- Little or no activity
- Wet monsoon
- Dry monsoon

Two-Point Equidistant Projection

14. **For which of the following activities is the majority of the land in India used?**
    A. nomadic herding
    B. subsistence farming
    C. manufacturing and trade
    D. commercial farming

15. **In which direction do the dry monsoons tend to move?**
    A. to the northwest
    B. to the northeast
    C. to the southeast
    D. to the southwest

16. **Which Asian country lies along the equator?**
    A. China
    B. India
    C. Indonesia
    D. Saudi Arabia

17. **For what purpose is *most* of the land in Kazakhstan used?**
    A. livestock raising
    B. commercial farming
    C. subsistence farming
    D. commercial fishing

Name_____ Class_____ Date _____

Middle Grades Test 2 — Visual Analysis

Directions: *Use the time line below to answer questions 1–5.*

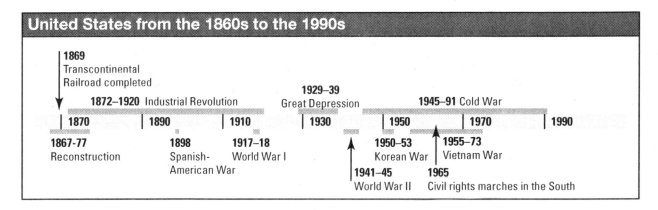

1. **According to the time line which sequence of events is correct?**

   A. Spanish-American War; Industrial Revolution; World War II; Great Depression

   B. Reconstruction; Great Depression; Korean War; Vietnam War

   C. Great Depression; World War I; Cold War; Industrial Revolution

   D. World War I; World War II; Great Depression; Korean War

2. **Which of the following statements is true, based on the information in the time line?**

   A. Between 1910 and 1970, the United States experienced six wars.

   B. The end of the Great Depression was marked by the beginning of World War I.

   C. At the end of World War I, the Industrial Revolution had nearly ended.

   D. The Korean War and the Vietnam War overlapped by two years.

3. **Which of the following events occurred during the Cold War?**

   A. World War II

   B. the Great Depression

   C. the Vietnam War

   D. the Industrial Revolution

4. **During which of the following periods did civil rights marches in the South occur?**

   A. Reconstruction

   B. World War I

   C. the Great Depression

   D. the Cold War

5. **Which event on the time line spans the *greatest* amount of time?**

   A. Great Depression

   B. Transcontinental Railroad completed

   C. Industrial Revolution

   D. Korean War

Middle Grades Test 2 — Visual Analysis (continued)

Directions: *Examine the cartoon below, and answer questions 6–10.*

6. **Who or what do the people in the water represent?**
   A. They represent people who have jumped in before knowing how to swim.
   B. They represent Russians invading U.S. shorelines.
   C. They represent immigrants coming to the United States.
   D. They represent big business in America.

7. **Who or what does the lifeguard represent?**
   A. He represents the European Union.
   B. He represents the United States Coast Guard.
   C. He represents American immigrants.
   D. He represents the United States government.

8. **Which of the following would be the *best* caption for this cartoon?**
   A. "Who taught these people how to speak English?"
   B. "Uncle Sam realizes he can't swim."
   C. "Can America save everyone?"
   D. "The war against terrorism comes to America's shores."

9. **Which of the following scenes presents the message *most* similar to the one depicted in the cartoon?**
   A. A woman dressed as the Statue of Liberty looks sadly at a long line of children carrying empty bowls as she ladles the last of her pot of oatmeal to the first child in line.
   B. The President of the United States shakes hands with the president of another nation.
   C. An older man and woman sit on a park bench smiling and laughing as they toss bread to a flock of hungry pigeons.
   D. A well-dressed man and woman look away as they walk past a long line of homeless people begging for money.

10. **Which of the following statements *best* explains the symbolism in this cartoon?**
    A. The umbrella is a symbol that represents the sky.
    B. The chair is a symbol that represents big business.
    C. The word *Help* is a symbol that represents English-speaking immigrants.
    D. The life preserver is a symbol that represents American aid.

Name_____ Class_____ Date _____

Middle Grades Test 3 — Critical Thinking and Reading

Directions: *Read the passage below. Then answer questions 1–4.*

At the Battle of Gettysburg in July 1863, both the North and the South suffered heavy casualties. On November 19, 1863, President Abraham Lincoln visited Gettysburg to dedicate the battlefield cemetery, and he delivered the following speech.

The Gettysburg Address

Four score and seven years ago our fathers brought forth on this continent, a new nation, conceived in liberty, and dedicated to the proposition that all men are created equal.

Now we are engaged in a great civil war, testing whether that nation, or any nation so conceived and so dedicated, can long endure. We are met on a great battlefield of that war. We have come to dedicate a portion of that field, as a final resting place for those who here gave their lives that that nation might live. It is altogether fitting and proper that we should do this. But in a larger sense, we cannot dedicate—we cannot consecrate—we cannot hallow—this ground. The brave men, living and dead, who struggled here have consecrated it, far above our poor power to add or detract. The world will little note, nor long remember what we say here, but it can never forget what they did here. It is for us the living, rather, to be dedicated here to the unfinished work which they who fought here have thus far so nobly advanced. It is rather for us to be here dedicated to the great task remaining before us—that from these honored dead we take increased devotion to that cause for which they gave the last full measure of devotion—that we here highly resolve that these dead shall not have died in vain—that this nation, under God, shall have a new birth of freedom—and that government of the people, by the people, for the people shall not perish from the earth.

---

1. **What does President Lincoln say is the *best* way to honor the soldiers who have died at the Battle of Gettysburg?**
    A. Attack the enemy forces on the great battlefield of Gettysburg.
    B. Keep alive the principles of democracy that they died for.
    C. Seek immediate revenge on those who would threaten democracy.
    D. Refuse to be drawn into another meaningless war.

2. **What is the "unfinished work" that President Lincoln believes the American people still have to do?**
    A. They need to ensure that the principles of our nation do not fail.
    B. They need to consecrate the soldiers who have fought in all wars.
    C. They need to continue to expand America's borders.
    D. They need to ensure that foreign nations do not destroy the Union.

3. **What is the *most likely* effect of President Lincoln's speech?**
    A. Listeners will be discouraged from supporting the war effort.
    B. The government of the United States will be dissolved.
    C. Congress will withdraw support for a memorial at Gettysburg.
    D. Listeners will have greater dedication to Lincoln's cause.

4. **What might have been one reason that President Lincoln chose to give a speech about the future of the nation when dedicating the Gettysburg cemetery?**
    A. to consecrate the ground in memory of the dead soldiers
    B. to emphasize both that no one died in vain, and that we must continue the fight
    C. to encourage young men to fight for freedom by enlisting
    D. to cause families to fear that their sons might perish in the war

Name_____ Class _____ Date _____

Middle Grades Test 3 — Critical Thinking and Reading (continued)

Directions: *Read the story "The Envious Buffalo" from*
The Fables of India, *retold by Joseph Gaer. Then answer questions 5–8.*

On a small farm in southern India there lived a water buffalo named Big Red Bubalus with his younger brother named Little Red Bubalus. These two brothers did all the hard work on the farm. They plowed and they harrowed; they seeded; and they brought in the harvest for their owner.

Yet for all their labors they were rarely rewarded. And all they were given to eat was grass and straw, or chaff when the grain was husked.

This same farmer owned a pig who did nothing but eat and wallow in the water pumped up for him by the buffaloes. Yet the hog was fed on rice and millet and was well taken care of by the farmer and his family.

Little Red Bubalus complained to his brother: "We, who do all the hard work, are treated shabbily and our master gives us next to nothing to eat. Most of the time we have to go out into the pasture to find our own food. Yet this lazy pig is fed all the time and never does any work."

"Envy him not, little brother," said Big Red Bubalus. . . .

One day the farmer's only daughter was engaged to be married. And as the wedding day drew near, the hog was slaughtered and roasted for the wedding feast.

Then Big Red Bubalus said to Little Red Bubalus, "Now do you see why a pig is not to be envied?"

And Little Red Bubalus replied, "Yes, now I understand. It is better to feed on straw and chaff, and to live out our lives, than to be fattened on rice only to end up on a roasting spit."

5. This story is a fable that teaches a lesson about life called a *moral*. What is the moral of this story?
   A. Do not waste time working when you can rest.
   B. Do not wish for what you can never have.
   C. We should not envy others but should appreciate the good in our own lives.
   D. Only buffaloes have to suffer.

6. What happens after Little Red Bubalus complains?
   A. Big Red Bubalus says nothing.
   B. Big Red Bubalus responds, "Envy him not, little brother."
   C. The pig is rewarded with rice and millet.
   D. Big Red Bubalus is punished.

7. the pig : _____ :: the buffaloes : _____
   A. business people, rich people
   B. young people, old people
   C. leisurely people, hard-working people
   D. messy people, neat people

8. How does understanding the situation help Little Red Bubalus?
   A. It helps Little Red Bubalus understand that he will someday be like the pig.
   B. It helps Little Red Bubalus understand that Big Red Bubalus is wrong.
   C. It helps Little Red Bubalus understand that his work will be rewarded.
   D. It helps Little Red Bubalus understand that now he will be fed millet.

Middle Grades Test 3 — Critical Thinking and Reading *(continued)*

Directions: *Read the passage below that describes the Korean martial art of tae kwon do. Then answer questions 9–12.*

The martial arts are ways of fighting . . . but a person who [practices the martial arts] tries to act in ways that bring peace. [Those who practice the martial arts] do not fight in real life unless there is no other choice. Koreans developed the martial art of tae kwon do more than 2,000 years ago. Today, it is one of the most popular martial arts in the world.

The name *tae kwon do* means "the art of kicking and punching." Tae kwon do is especially famous for its jumping and spinning kicks. Before they can do a kick, however, students must block or move out of the way of kicks and punches that are coming toward them. Students of tae kwon do combine quick, straight movements with circular, flowing movements.

To students of tae kwon do, their art is more than a way to defend themselves. It is a way of life. Students learn the following rules:

- be loyal to your country, your school, and your friends
- respect your family, your teachers, and your elders
- maintain a strong spirit and never give up
- finish what you begin

Tae kwon do students promise to follow these rules. They also vow to work hard and keep up with schoolwork. But most of all, they commit themselves to behaving in ways that are kind and peaceful.

9. **Which of the following statements best characterizes tae kwon do?**
   A. It is a martial art that teaches you how to defend yourself without having to work out solutions with your enemy.
   B. It is a martial art that allows people to learn new ways to harm their enemies.
   C. It is a martial art that teaches students how to defend themselves and how to live their lives in a peaceful way.
   D. It is a martial art that involves commitment and sacrifice without loyalty to any one nation or ruler.

10. **Which of the following people is following the lessons taught in tae kwon do?**
    A. Despite getting low grades on his spelling test last week, Juan studied even harder for his test the following week.
    B. Marguerite told her older brother that her middle school was the worst in the city.
    C. Aaron practiced his kicks all evening, even though he promised his mother he would spend the evening studying.
    D. Instead of finishing her homework, Rachel went to the pep rally to root for her friends on the football team.

11. **If someone thought that tae kwon do involved jumping into a fighting ring and kicking your opponent as many times as possible, in what way would he or she be wrong?**
    A. Tae kwon do is a way to defend oneself, but it is more than that because it is also a way of life.
    B. Tae kwon do students must spend most of their time studying and thinking.
    C. Tae kwon do is a way of life, and those who practice it today never use it for fighting.
    D. Tae kwon do is not fought in a ring anymore, but fighters still do this if it is necessary.

12. **How might tae kwon do help provide the discipline necessary for one to lead a successful life?**
    A. Tae kwon do teaches students that physical strength is important.
    B. Tae kwon do improves one's intelligence.
    C. Tae kwon do forbids students from fighting.
    D. Tae kwon do teaches students not to give up and always to do their best.

Middle Grades Test 3 — Critical Thinking and Reading (continued)

Directions: *The passage below is from Louis L'Amour's book,* Frontier. *It is a book of essays and photos about frontiers. This passage is from the last essay in the book, "The Eternal Frontier." Read the passage below. Then answer questions 13–16.*

The question I am most often asked is, "Where is the frontier now?" The answer should be obvious. Our frontier lies in outer space. Outer space is a frontier without end, the eternal frontier, an everlasting challenge to explorers not [only] of other planets and other solar systems but also of the mind of man.

One might ask—why outer space, when so much remains to be done here? If that had been the spirit of man we would still be hunters and food gatherers, growling over the bones of carrion in a cave somewhere. It is our destiny to move out, to accept the challenge, to dare the unknown.

Yet we must not forget that along the way to outer space whole industries are springing into being that did not exist before. The computer age has arisen in part from the space effort. . . . Transistors, chips, integrated circuits, Teflon, new medicines, new ways of treating diseases, new ways of performing operations, all these and a multitude of other developments that enable man to live and to live better are linked to the space effort. Most of these developments have been so incorporated into our day-to-day life that they are taken for granted. . . .

If we are content to live in the past, we have no future. And today is the past.

13. **Which of the following statements *best* expresses the author's viewpoint?**
   A. There is no reason to explore outer space.
   B. If we explore outer space, there will be new developments in technology.
   C. If we do not explore outer space, we are living in the past.
   D. There is so much to do on Earth that we should not explore outer space.

14. **What is different about life now than before the space effort?**
   A. Now we have transistors, microchips, and new ways of treating diseases.
   B. We are no longer hunters and gatherers living in caves.
   C. Now we take many developments for granted.
   D. We are no longer content to live in the past.

15. **According to the passage, which of the following ideas would the author *most likely* encourage to convince more people to support the space effort?**
   A. Have schools teach more about outer space.
   B. Have schools teach more about the past.
   C. Publicize all the developments that are linked to the space effort.
   D. Take away people's computers for a day.

16. **With which statement would the author *most likely* disagree?**
   A. The space effort is an important part of our future.
   B. The space effort has had no effect on most people's lives.
   C. The space effort has affected how we live today.
   D. The space effort has improved people's lives.

Middle Grades Test 4 — Communications

Directions: *Read the following passage. Then answer questions 1–3.*

As in America, Japanese elementary and secondary schools run from first to twelfth grade. But as far as similarities go, that is about it.

To begin with, Japan's school year runs two months longer than America's. Japanese students go to school Monday through Friday, with a half day on Saturday. Altogether, they attend school 240 days out of the year, compared with the American average of 180. The Japanese have one spring vacation and one summer vacation, each three weeks long. . . .

After school, 80 percent of the students attend juku, or "cram school," for extra study, or they have private tutors. They do this to prepare for Japan's rigorous system of entrance exams. Students are free to attend any school they wish as long as they pass its admittance test. The best schools have the most demanding exams. . . .

Few American students would find the Japanese system desirable. But it produces results.

---

1. **Which of the following statements *best* supports the conclusion of this passage?**

   A. Japanese students study history, economics, and literature during their high school years.

   B. Ten percent of all Chinese students attend college at Japanese universities, which are highly regarded.

   C. According to a study by Stanford University, more U.S. students are attending colleges today than in the past.

   D. An estimated 94 percent of Japanese students graduate from high school, compared with less than 80 percent of U.S. students.

2. **In a comparison chart based on this passage, which of the following column titles would be followed by the *most* entries?**

   A. Ways Japanese Education Is Different From U.S. Education

   B. Ways U.S. Education Is Similar to Japanese Education

   C. Ways High School Is Different From Middle School

   D. Ways the Japanese School Day Is Different From the U.S. School Day

3. **Michiko is an exchange student from Japan. She is in your class, but she seems to be several years ahead of you and your classmates in her studies. Which of the following is the *best* conclusion you can make about this observation, based on the information in the passage?**

   A. It may not be accurate because you cannot compare Michiko's studies to those of her American classmates.

   B. It may be accurate because Michiko has likely spent more time in class and faced stricter requirements than American students her age.

   C. It may be accurate because Michiko may be several years older, as most Japanese students are.

   D. It may not be accurate because Michiko may not be ahead of her classmates in her home country.

Middle Grades Test 4 — Communications *(continued)*

Directions: *Read the passage below. Then answer questions 4–7.*

The Great Serpent Mound

The serpent mound in Ohio served a very different purpose from that of Cahokia's pyramid mounds. The twisting, snakelike structure was a cemetery. Called the Great Serpent Mound, it is just one of many similar mounds in Ohio. When you look at these mounds from above, they are shaped like animals. Some served as graves for as many as 1,000 people.

The mounds also hold some of the precious belongings of the Mound Builders. Researchers probing the serpent mounds have found jewelry made of shell and copper, clay statues, and other works of art. Some of these items are made from materials that are not from Ohio. Therefore, researchers believe that the Mound Builders must have been involved in extensive trading.

---

4. You are an archaeologist digging at a site in Illinois. You uncover a beautiful clay pot. After some study, you determine that the paint material used to decorate the pot is not from the Illinois area. Using the same reasoning that is presented in the passage, what would you *most likely* conclude?
   A. The pot is part of a mass grave system in the shape of an animal.
   B. The pot is not part of the Great Serpent Mound.
   C. The pot was painted with materials received by trade.
   D. The pot is from Cahokia's pyramid mounds.

5. For what purpose was the Great Serpent Mound built?
   A. It was used as a temple.
   B. It was used for flood prevention.
   C. It was used as a burial ground.
   D. It was used in religious ceremonies.

6. Jennifer's class studied the Mound Builders, and now she wants to go to Ohio to see the Great Serpent Mound for herself. In an effort to persuade her mother to take her there for a weekend vacation, she pleads, "Mom, please, we have to go! The Great Serpent Mound is the only one ever built." Jennifer's mother could dispute this argument using what piece of information from the passage?
   A. The Great Serpent Mound is no longer in Ohio, but it is now in Wisconsin.
   B. The Great Serpent Mound is just one of many similar mounds in Ohio.
   C. The Great Serpent Mound is very similar to Cahokia's pyramid mounds.
   D. The Great Serpent Mound takes much longer than a weekend to locate.

7. According to the passage, which of the following is a true statement about the Mound Builders?
   A. They did not bury their dead.
   B. A complex system of canals was used to move dirt.
   C. They were known for burying their enemies alive.
   D. They lived in what is now the central part of the United States.

Middle Grades Test 4 — Communications *(continued)*

Directions: *Study the following table. Then answer questions 8–10.*

Rival Plans for Reconstruction				
Plan	**Ten Percent Plan**	**Wade-Davis Bill**	**Johnson Plan**	**Reconstruction Act**
Proposed by	President Abraham Lincoln (1863)	Republicans in Congress (1864)	President Andrew Johnson (1865)	Radical Republicans (1867)
Conditions for Former Confederate States to Rejoin Union	■ 10 percent of voters must swear loyalty to Union ■ Must abolish slavery	■ Majority of white men must swear loyalty ■ Former Confederate volunteers cannot vote or hold office	■ Majority of white men must swear loyalty ■ Must ratify Thirteenth Amendment ■ Former Confederate officials may vote and hold office	■ Must disband state governments ■ Must write new constitutions ■ Must ratify Fourteenth Amendment ■ African American men must be allowed to vote

8. **Which of the plans listed in the table would have punished the Confederate states *most* severely?**

   A. Ten Percent Plan

   B. Wade-Davis Bill

   C. Johnson Plan

   D. Reconstruction Act

9. **If you discovered that this table had been compiled by a former Confederate soldier, what might you suspect about it?**

   A. The information is not current because it is over 100 years old and the soldier is dead.

   B. The information is probably not biased because the soldier has no personal interest in which option is chosen.

   C. The information may be biased because the soldier will be affected directly by the conditions.

   D. The information lacks authority because a soldier is unable to compile facts.

10. **You are politically active during the Reconstruction era, and you are making a speech to a group of citizens. In your speech, you argue that slavery must be abolished in the United States, that Southern white men must swear loyalty to the Union, and that state governments should be excused from writing new constitutions. You also say that African Americans should not be allowed to vote, but that former Confederate officials can. Which of the following plans would you *most likely* support?**

    A. Ten Percent Plan

    B. Johnson Plan

    C. Wade-Davis Bill

    D. Reconstruction Act

Middle Grades Test 4 — Communications *(continued)*

Directions: *Look at the table below. Then answer questions 11–16.*

World War II Deaths

	Military Dead	Civilian Dead
Britain	264,000	93,000
France	213,000	350,000
Soviet Union	7,500,000	15,000,000
United States	292,000	*
Germany	3,500,000	780,000
Italy	242,000	153,000
Japan	1,300,000	672,000

* Very small number
All figures are estimates.
Source: *Encyclopaedia Britannica*

11. In a report detailing the human losses incurred during the war, Justin wanted to note which country suffered the *most* casualties during World War II. What should his report say about total casualties?
    A. The United States suffered more casualties than any other nation.
    B. The Soviet Union suffered more casualties than any other nation.
    C. Britain suffered more casualties than any other nation.
    D. France suffered more casualties than any other nation.

12. In which country was the difference between the number of military deaths and the number of civilian deaths the *greatest*?
    A. Germany   C. Britain
    B. Japan   D. Soviet Union

13. The number of U.S. civilian dead was such a small number that it wasn't estimated on this chart. Which of the following countries had the fewest number of civilian dead compared to its military dead?
    A. Soviet Union C. Japan
    B. Germany   D. Italy

14. Using this table in a report he gave to his history class, Juan said, "Despite having 292,000 military casualties, the United States had very few civilian casualties. Its ally, the Soviet Union, had exactly 7,500,000 military dead and exactly 15,000,000 civilians dead during the war." What is wrong with Juan's statement?
    A. The figures about the war deaths are incorrect.
    B. The United States had a significant number of civilian deaths.
    C. The figures in the table are estimates, so the number of Soviet deaths is not exact.
    D. The Soviet Union suffered more military deaths than civilian deaths.

15. According to the information in the table, which of the following could you *most likely* conclude?
    A. Given the number of military deaths, many battles were probably fought in the United States.
    B. Given Italy's relatively low number of casualties, Italian soldiers were probably highly skilled.
    C. Given the high number of casualties, the Soviet Union probably started the war.
    D. Given the number of civilian deaths, many battles were probably fought in Germany and the Soviet Union.

16. Which of the following countries is estimated to have twice as many military deaths as civilian deaths during World War II?
    A. Britain
    B. Japan
    C. United States
    D. France

Name_____ Class_____ Date _____

Middle Grades Test 4 — Communications (continued)

Directions: *Examine the two graphs below. Then answer questions 17–20.*

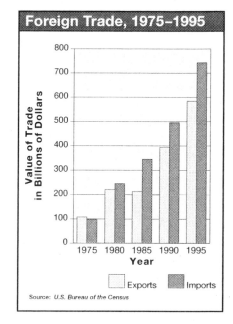

17. **Compare both graphs about foreign trade in the United States. Which of the following statements about the graphs is true?**
    A. Since 1865, the average value of U.S. foreign trade has remained the same.
    B. In general, from 1865 to 1915 and from 1975 to 1995, the value of U.S. foreign trade has steadily risen.
    C. The difference between the amount the United States exports and the amount it imports has been roughly equal since 1856.
    D. Between 1975 and 1995, the United States generally exported more goods than it imported.

18. **According to the information in the two graphs, what can you accurately conclude about the period between 1916 and 1974?**
    A. The trend must have changed because that is what trends do.
    B. The value in billions of dollars continued to increase each year, resulting in an upward, positive trend.
    C. Nothing; information about this time period is not shown in the graphs.
    D. The trend was similar, and the trade deficit increased at or near the same rate between time periods.

19. **A trade surplus exists when a country exports more goods than it imports. In which of the following years did the United States experience a trade surplus?**
    A. 1975   C. 1990
    B. 1980   D. 1995

20. **You have to write a report about U.S. foreign trade, and you want to include the difference between the goods the United States sells to other countries and the goods it buys from other countries over a single ten-year time period. Which graph would be *best* to include in your report and why?**
    A. The bar graph would be better to use because it includes trade by imports and exports.
    B. The bar graph would be better to use because its information is more current than the information in the line graph.
    C. The line graph would be better to use because the results include the value of trade in billions of dollars.
    D. The line graph would be better to use because it breaks down trade into ten-year periods.

Middle Grades Test 5 — Vocabulary

Directions: *Read the passage. Then answer the questions that follow the passage. Mark the letter of the best answer to each question.*

Many people believe that Benjamin Franklin flew a kite in a thunderstorm to prove that lightning was electrical. Scientists debate with each other whether this incident really happened. According to legend, Franklin tied a key to a kite, flew the kite in a thunderstorm, and waited for lightning to strike the key. If he had performed the experiment in this way, he most likely would have been injured if not killed!

It is true that Ben Franklin performed experiments with electricity, and his discoveries contributed to that field of science. Considering Franklin's knowledge about electricity, many scientists doubt he would have attempted the dangerous kite experiment.

1. **Which word could replace the word *incident* in the passage?**
   A. idea
   B. event
   C. dream
   D. mistake

2. ***Debate* means**
   A. wonder.
   B. agree.
   C. explain.
   D. argue.

3. **The opposite of *contributed* is**
   A. blamed.
   B. subtracted.
   C. known.
   D. helped.

4. ***Injured* means**
   A. hurt.
   B. destroyed.
   C. paid.
   D. challenged.

Middle Grades Test 5 — Vocabulary *(continued)*

Directions: *Read the passage. Then answer the questions that follow the passage. Mark the letter of the best answer to each question.*

The Grand Canyon is one of the most fascinating natural <u>features</u> in North America. It was <u>created</u> by the Colorado River cutting through the high plateaus of northern Arizona. Each year people from all over the world decide to go hiking there. People who hike the Grand Canyon face many challenges. First, of course, they face a long hike down. Later, they face a long climb back to the top. Hikers easily become tired and thirsty in the canyon's desert climate. People who plan to hike and camp in the Grand Canyon need to carry plenty of water and protection from the sun because they will be constantly <u>exposed</u> to the <u>elements</u>.

---

5. **An antonym for** *create* **is**
   A. damage.
   B. destroy.
   C. deny.
   D. design.

6. **Another way to say "the Grand Canyon is one of the most fascinating natural *features* in North America" is**
   A. The Grand Canyon is one of the most fascinating landforms in North America.
   B. The Grand Canyon is one of the most fascinating parks in North America.
   C. The Grand Canyon is one of the most fascinating symbols in North America.
   D. The Grand Canyon is one of the most fascinating experiences in North America.

7. **As it is used in the passage, the word** *exposed* **is the opposite of**
   A. uncovered.
   B. protected.
   C. visible.
   D. aware.

8. **In the passage, the word** *elements* **refers to**
   A. the land.
   B. the water.
   C. the weather.
   D. the schools.

Middle Grades Test 5 — Vocabulary *(continued)*

Directions: *Read the passage. Then answer the questions that follow the passage. Mark the letter of the best answer to each question.*

The United States currently gets most of its energy from fossil fuels, such as coal, oil, and natural gas. However, the supply of fossil fuels is limited. If we continue to use these fuels at the current rate, we may <u>eventually</u> use up our supply. Also, fossil fuels release pollution into the atmosphere when they are used. As an alternative, many people have looked for ways to <u>expand</u> our sources of energy and make use of the sun and wind. These are energy sources that will never run out, and they do not pollute. These types of energy have <u>definite</u> drawbacks, too. The equipment used to catch solar and wind power is expensive, and not all <u>communities</u> receive enough sunlight or wind to make energy this way.

---

9. *Eventually* means

   A. rapidly.

   B. sooner or later.

   C. within ten years.

   D. time and again.

10. **The opposite of *expand* is**

   A. determine.

   B. shrink.

   C. enjoy.

   D. affect.

11. **In the passage, the word *communities* probably means**

   A. continents.

   B. large families.

   C. cultures.

   D. towns and cities.

12. **If something is *definite*, it is**

   A. misunderstood.

   B. popular.

   C. well-defined.

   D. unimportant.

Middle Grades Test 5 — Vocabulary *(continued)*

Directions: *Read the passage. Then answer the questions that follow the passage. Mark the letter of the best answer to each question.*

> People who do <u>research</u> on whales are learning fascinating facts about how these animals <u>communicate</u>. Like many other mammals, whales communicate by making sounds only other whales can understand. All whales communicate in <u>similar</u> ways. However, different <u>species</u> of whales, such as blue whales and humpback whales, make different sounds. Whales can chirp, click, squeak, and whistle. These whale "songs" can travel long distances through the water.
>
> Whales also use body language to communicate. Sometimes they swim in certain ways or slap the surface of the water with their tails. For people, these actions may simply be entertaining. To whales, however, these actions have certain meaning.

13. If people do *research* on whales it means they

A. help whales.

B. study whales.

C. show whales.

D. release whales into the ocean.

14. In the passage, *communicate* means

A. touch.

B. eat.

C. swim.

D. talk.

15. The opposite of *similar* is

A. annoying.

B. normal.

C. dark.

D. different.

16. Which word could replace the word *species* in the phrase "different species of whales make different sounds?"

A. sizes

B. kinds

C. ages

D. friends

Middle Grades Test 6 — Writing

Directions: *Read the following passage. Then complete the activity.*

In school sports, field hockey is usually limited to girls while football is often considered a boys' game. Recently, some schools have allowed girls to play football on boys' teams. Some boys think that they should be allowed to play field hockey on girls' teams. They believe it is only fair to open all teams to students of both sexes.

Many people disagree, however, including some of the same people who think that girls should be allowed to play on football teams with boys. They note that most boys are bigger and stronger than girls. For this reason, allowing boys to play on girls' teams would be similar to allowing high school students to compete with middle school students. Some opponents also worry that boys tend to take over girls' teams. They believe that including boys would change girls' sports and cause girls to feel unsafe.

Decide how you feel about the rights of boys to play on girls' sports teams. Write a paragraph in which you state your opinion and give reasons to support your position.

_____

_____

_____

_____

_____

_____

_____

_____

_____

_____

_____

_____

_____

_____

_____

_____

_____

_____

_____

Middle Grades Test 6 — Writing *(continued)*

> People choose pets for different reasons. Many people believe that it is best to choose a pet that fits your individual lifestyle. Because dogs often require a lot of attention and exercise, dogs may be good pets for people who have large yards and enjoy spending their time walking and playing with an animal companion. People who live in apartments or lead quieter lives may prefer cats for pets.

Directions: *Compare two kinds of animals you might choose as pets and explain the similarities and differences between them. You might choose two animals that you would like to have as pets, or you might choose one animal that you would like more than the other. Include details that help you compare and contrast the two animals.*

_____

_____

_____

_____

_____

_____

_____

_____

_____

_____

_____

_____

_____

_____

_____

_____

_____

_____

_____

_____

_____

_____

_____

_____

Middle Grades Test 6 — Writing *(continued)*

Directions: *Read the passage. Then summarize the main idea of this passage in one or two sentences. Mention two or three facts that help support the main idea.*

Every year on the fourth Thursday of April, young people around the United States participate in Take Our Daughters and Sons to Work Day. This event was launched in 1993. At first, it was called Take Our Daughters to Work Day and was intended only for girls. Many people believed that this activity would help girls learn about new jobs and careers for the future. Allowing girls to go to work with their parents seemed to be a good way for girls to build self-esteem.

However, many people thought it was unfair to exclude boys, who need to think about their futures just as much as girls. The event was expanded to include them, too. For many families, Take Our Daughters and Sons to Work Day has become an important way for children to learn about job possibilities for their future and get a glimpse of their parents' roles in the workplace. It also gives children a chance to spend extra time with their parents.

_____

_____

_____

_____

_____

_____

_____

_____

_____

_____

_____

_____

_____

_____

_____

_____

_____

_____

_____

_____

Middle Grades Test 6 — Writing *(continued)*

Directions: *Read the passage. Then complete the activity that follows.*

Your school has regular fire drills, in which you learn which exits to use and where to meet outside in case of a fire. Does your family also have an emergency escape plan? Creating such a plan is one of the most important preparations your family can make in case of a fire. You should identify two possible exits from every room, one of which can be a window, and decide on a location away from the house where everyone will meet afterward. You should also make sure that everyone understands the following points. Do not try to put out a fire yourself, even if it's a small one. Instead, alert everyone in the house and leave immediately. Do not take anything with you, and do not go back inside the house. Go to a neighbor's house and call 911. If your clothes are on fire, stop, drop, and roll. Remind others to do the same. If there is smoke, stay low, even crawl if necessary, to stay below the smoke. Smoke can seriously damage your health. In addition to drawing up an escape plan, your family should hold a fire drill once or twice a year to make sure everyone knows what to do. Make sure that everyone recognizes the sound of a smoke detector and that your smoke detectors are working properly by testing them once a month and changing their batteries at least once a year.

Summarize the information above in an outline. One has been started for you below. Remember to give your outline a title.

Title:_____

  I. Create an emergency escape plan_____

    A. How to get out of the house_____

      1. Identify two exits from every room_____

    B. Location to meet away from the house_____

  II. Points to Remember in Case of a Fire_____

    A._____

_____

_____

_____

_____

_____

_____

_____

_____

_____

_____

_____

Name_____ Class_____ Date _____

High School Test 1 — Geographic Literacy

Directions: *Use the map of Africa to answer questions 1–4.*

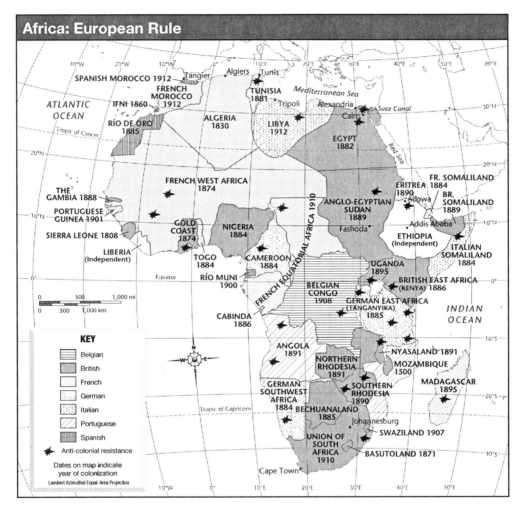

1. **Which two European countries controlled the *most* area in Africa?**

   A. Britain and France

   B. France and Portugal

   C. Germany and Britain

   D. Spain and Belgium

2. **Which of the following colonies had the *most* incidents of anti-colonial resistance?**

   A. Nigeria

   B. French West Africa

   C. Angola

   D. German East Africa

3. **What is significant about the year 1884 in Nigeria?**

   A. It was the year that Nigeria won an anti-colonial resistance war.

   B. It was the year that Nigeria gained its independence.

   C. It was the year that Nigeria was colonized by Britain.

   D. It was the year that Nigeria became ruled by the Belgians.

4. **Which city in Africa can be found at approximately 10°N, 40°E?**

   A. Fashoda   C. Cairo

   B. Addis Ababa D. Tangier

Name_____ Class_____ Date _____

High School Test 1 — Geographic Literacy *(continued)*

Directions: *Use the map of East Asia to answer questions 5–8.*

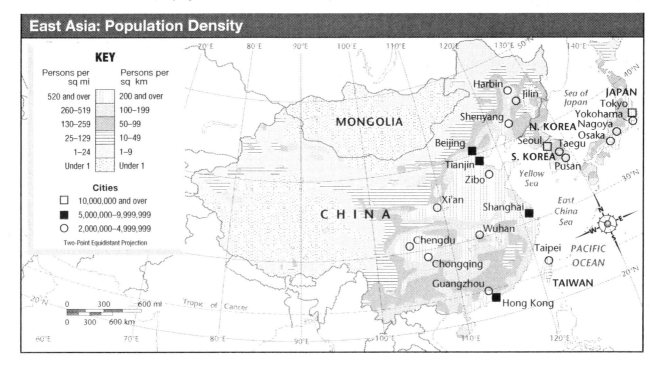

East Asia: Population Density

5. **Which of the following cities has the highest population?**
   A. Osaka, Japan
   B. Seoul, South Korea
   C. Taipei, Taiwan
   D. Hong Kong, China

6. **If you wanted to live in an area of East Asia with the fewest people per square mile, in which country should you live?**
   A. North Korea   C. South Korea
   B. Japan   D. Mongolia

7. **Which of the following countries lies northeast of 30°N, 120°E?**
   A. Japan   C. Taiwan
   B. China   D. Mongolia

8. **According to the information presented on the map, which of the following statements is true?**
   A. The cities with the highest number of people per square mile are located in the northeast corner of the region.
   B. The cities with the largest populations are found in the eastern regions of China and Japan.
   C. Most of Mongolia is inhabited by 1–24 people per square mile.
   D. The majority of western China is desert land, and the majority of eastern China is hills and valleys.

High School Test 1 — Geographic Literacy *(continued)*

Directions: *Use the map of Latin America to answer questions 9–13.*

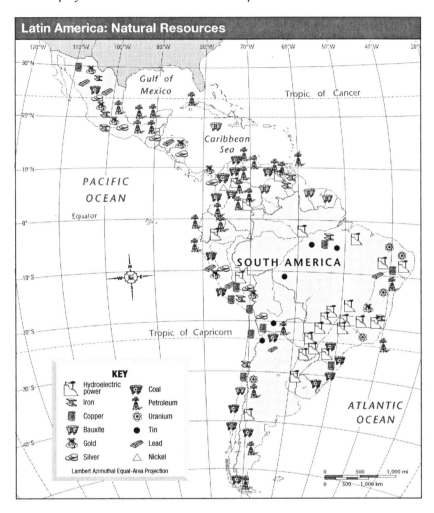

Latin America: Natural Resources

9. **Which of the following resources occurs *most frequently* in northern South America?**
   A. petroleum
   B. hydroelectric power
   C. gold
   D. uranium

10. **Which of the following natural resources is the *most common* along the Tropic of Capricorn?**
    A. gold
    B. hydroelectric power
    C. iron
    D. petroleum

11. **Which of the following natural resources is found at the southern tip of South America?**
    A. tin
    B. coal
    C. uranium
    D. iron

12. **Which of the following is the *most common* resource found around the Gulf of Mexico?**
    A. hydroelectric power
    B. petroleum
    C. coal
    D. iron

13. **In South America, where are the majority of petroleum resources located?**
    A. in the southwest
    B. in the southeast
    C. in the northwest
    D. in the northeast

Name_____ Class_____ Date _____

High School Test 1 — Geographic Literacy (continued)

Directions: *Use the following map to answer questions 14–18.*

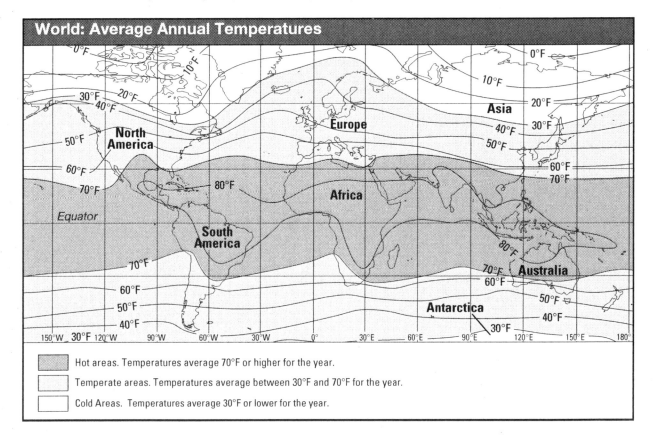

World: Average Annual Temperatures

Hot areas. Temperatures average 70°F or higher for the year.

Temperate areas. Temperatures average between 30°F and 70°F for the year.

Cold Areas. Temperatures average 30°F or lower for the year.

14. **Which entire continent has an average annual temperature range between 30°F and 70°F?**

    A. Europe   C. Australia

    B. Africa   D. South America

15. **What kind of average temperature would you expect at the southern tip of Africa?**

    A. hot   C. cold

    B. temperate   D. frigid

16. **According to this map, what average temperature would you find along the Equator?**

    A. 30°F–40°F   C. 60°F–70°F

    B. 40°F–50°F   D. 70°F or higher

17. **Which of the following words *best* describes the average annual temperature of Antarctica?**

    A. hot   C. cool

    B. warm   D. cold

18. **Which part of the world has the coolest average temperatures?**

    A. the regions closest to the Equator

    B. the regions farthest from the Equator

    C. the regions along 0° longitude

    D. the western region of Europe

High School Test 2 — Visual Analysis

Directions: *Read the paragraph that follows and use the posters to answer questions 1–4.*

During World War I and World War II, the United States government ran campaigns to publicize the war effort and build support. The poster of the women was produced during World War I, and the poster of the men was produced during World War II.

1. **What is the intended main message of both posters?**
   A. The posters are asking men and women to join the armed services.
   B. The posters are asking men and women to always wear their uniforms properly.
   C. The posters are asking men and women to support the war effort on the home front.
   D. The posters are asking men and women to respect the men in the armed services.

2. **In the poster on the right, who does the man in the overalls represent?**
   A. a soldier   C. a German
   B. a farmer   D. the President

3. **The World War I poster was used to inspire**
   A. women.   C. war objectors.
   B. draft evaders.   D. invalids.

4. **Which of the following descriptions of a possible poster conveys the same message as these posters?**
   A. a picture of a man wearing a fast-food uniform taking an order from an American woman with the slogan "She'll Take Large Fries!"
   B. a picture of a woman in overalls riding a tractor and waving to a man in an army uniform with the slogan "Bring 'Em Back Alive!"
   C. a picture of a woman in a Navy uniform saluting a man in an Army uniform with the slogan "The Armed Services Need You!"
   D. a picture of a woman working at an airport security checkpoint with the slogan "Security on the Home Front Is Everyone's Job!"

High School Test 2 — Visual Analysis (continued)

Directions: *Use the graphs to answer questions 5–7.*

Economic Impact of the Great Depression

Unemployment 1925–1933

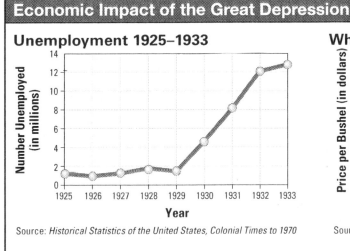

Source: *Historical Statistics of the United States, Colonial Times to 1970*

Wheat Prices 1925–1933

Source: *Historical Statistics of the United States, Colonial Times to 1970*

Stock Prices 1925–1933

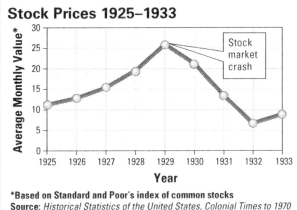

*Based on Standard and Poor's index of common stocks
Source: *Historical Statistics of the United States, Colonial Times to 1970*

Bank Suspensions 1925–1933

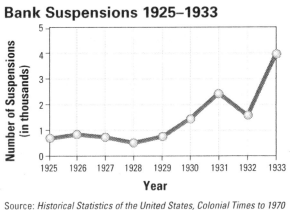

Source: *Historical Statistics of the United States, Colonial Times to 1970*

5. According to these graphs, what events occurred following the stock market crash?

A. Employment sharply rose, wheat prices increased, and bank suspensions declined.

B. Unemployment sharply rose, wheat prices declined, and bank suspensions declined.

C. Unemployment sharply rose, wheat prices declined, and bank suspensions rose.

D. Unemployment fell dramatically, wheat prices declined, and bank suspensions rose.

6. Between 1929 and 1932, the approximate number of unemployed people increased by

A. 10 million.

B. 4 million.

C. 11,000.

D. 14 million.

7. During the year that stock prices were at their highest, what was the price of wheat?

A. $.10 per bushel

B. $.50 per bushel

C. $1.00 per bushel

D. $10.00 per bushel

High School Test 3 — Critical Thinking and Reading

Directions: *Read the passage below. Then answer questions 1–4.*

Every four years, the American people vote for President. In recent decades, though, fewer and fewer people have actually cast their votes. In the 2004 election, only 64 percent of all Americans who could vote for President did so.

Many people are concerned about this trend, especially when they compare voter turnout in the United States to turnout in other countries. In Canada, 76 percent of all eligible voters vote. In Australia, Austria, Belgium, Italy, and Iceland, 90 percent or more of the voters take part in elections. Why do fewer people vote in the United States?

Some say that the problem is registration laws in the United States. In other countries, the government takes steps to register voters, and almost all possible voters are registered. In the United States, it is the people themselves who must make the effort to register. Here only about 70 percent of those who are able to vote actually register to vote.

Others say that the reason for low voter turnout is that the two main political parties in the United States are too similar. Many voters think there is not enough difference between them, and so they do not bother voting. These analysts point out that in 1992, when a strong third-party candidate ran for President, voter turnout increased over that in the previous election.

The fact that Americans often move is another problem. In the United States, it is state governments that register voters. A person who moves to a state just before an election may not have lived in the state long enough to meet the state residence requirements. He or she may not know where to go to register. As long as he or she is not registered, the person cannot vote in an election—even for President.

1. **The author might suggest improving voter turnout through all but which of the following measures?**
   A. informing new community residents of local voter registration sites
   B. implementing automatic government registration of all eligible voters
   C. preserving the dominance of the two main political parties
   D. passing less strict residence requirements

2. **The author contrasts which two things in this passage?**
   A. Presidential and non-Presidential elections
   B. voter turnout in the United States and other nations
   C. main-party and third-party candidates
   D. state and national residence requirements

3. **Which of the following statements from the passage expresses an opinion?**
   A. In Canada, 76 percent of all eligible voters vote.
   B. Every four years, the American people vote for President.
   C. In the United States, it is the people themselves who must make the effort to register.
   D. The reason for low voter turnout is that the two main political parties are too similar.

4. **What is the main idea of this passage?**
   A. The United States lags behind other nations in voter turnout.
   B. The United States should adopt a three-party system to improve voter turnout.
   C. A variety of factors contribute to the problem of low voter turnout in the United States.
   D. The U.S. federal government should be responsible for registering voters.

High School Test 3 — Critical Thinking and Reading (continued)

Directions: *Read the following passage. Then answer questions 5 and 6.*

After Abraham Lincoln's death, the task of Reconstruction [bringing the country back together] fell to President Andrew Johnson. In his first annual message to Congress, on December 4, 1865, Johnson explained the reasons for his Reconstruction policy:

"There is need for a spirit of mutual agreement and goodwill. All parties in the late terrible conflict must work together in harmony. On the one side, there must be a willingness to forgive and forget the disorders of the past. On the other side, the desire to maintain the Union shall be put beyond any doubt by the ratification of the proposed Thirteenth Amendment to the Constitution, which provides for the abolition of slavery forever within the limits of our country. The adoption of the amendment reunites us beyond all power of disruption. It heals the wound that is still imperfectly closed. It removes slavery, the element of which has so long confused and divided the country. It makes us once more a united people."

5. **According to President Johnson, what would ensure the reunification of the United States during the Reconstruction period?**
   A. the adoption of the Thirteenth Amendment
   B. the punishment of Confederate leaders
   C. the cooperation of northerners and southerners
   D. the rebuilding of the South

6. **With which statement would Johnson *most likely* disagree?**
   A. Representatives of the North and South should work together to govern the nation.
   B. Slavery should never be permitted in the United States.
   C. Regional disagreements that led to the Civil War should be forgotten.
   D. Those citizens who fought for the South should be punished severely.

7. **A United States congresswoman wants to accurately determine the opinions of her constituents on an important issue being considered in the House of Representatives. Which of the following would be the *most* reliable method for obtaining that information?**
   A. reading letters and e-mail messages about the issue from concerned constituents
   B. making a public appearance in her district and discussing the issue with people she meets
   C. conducting a telephone survey of randomly selected residents of her district regarding the issue
   D. meeting with members of her staff to consider the public's perception of the issue

High School Test 3 — Critical Thinking and Reading (continued)

Directions: *Read the passage below. Then answer questions 8 and 9.*

The 1780s saw a great deal of debate over where the capital city of the new nation should be located. Supporters of New York City, Philadelphia, Trenton, Wilmington, and Baltimore fought bitterly. However, no site could be found that was acceptable to a majority of the members of Congress.

Richard Bland Lee, a congressman from Virginia, suggested that the capital be built along the Potomac River. Massachusetts congressman Theodore Sedgwick opposed the idea:

It is the opinion of the eastern states that the climate of the Patowmack is not only unhealthy, but destructive to [the physical well-being of northerners]. . . . Vast numbers of eastern adventurers have gone to the Southern states, and all have found their graves there.

George Washington owned 20,000 acres on the Potomac River. For years he had tried to open the Potomac for navigation around Georgetown. He urged area merchants to write to Congress, denying that the Potomac was unhealthy. Alexander Hamilton persuaded northern members of Congress to support the Potomac location. Finally a deal was made. The capital would extend along the Potomac from the Eastern Branch northwest to Georgetown.

8. **Place the following items in the sequence in which they occurred.**

   1. Congress considers several northern cities as possible locations for a new capital.
   2. Congress selects the Potomac location for the capital.
   3. Alexander Hamilton asks northern Congressmen to support the Potomac location.
   4. Congressmen complain that the Potomac location is unhealthy.

   A. 2, 1, 3, 4
   B. 1, 4, 3, 2
   C. 1, 3, 2, 4
   D. 4, 1, 2, 3

9. **With which statement would Congressman Sedgwick *most likely* agree?**

   A. A location in the North would prove less dangerous to the health of government officials.
   B. The Potomac location would be too far removed from other major U.S. cities.
   C. The amount of land at the Potomac site would be insufficient for the construction of the nation's capital.
   D. George Washington should be given the authority to decide the location of the new capital.

High School Test 3 — Critical Thinking and Reading (continued)

Directions: *Read the following passage. Then answer questions 10 and 11.*

In the years after World War II, the southern states—mainly agricultural, often poor—suddenly exploded into growth and prosperity. Writers in the 1970s used the term "Sunbelt" to describe this change. . . . The key reason for Sunbelt growth was jobs, both new and transplanted. New manufacturing industries were started in the South or moved there from other areas. Sunbelt cities such as Houston, Dallas, and Atlanta grew quickly, with more room to spread out than crowded metropolitan areas in the North. People flocked to the area, leaving behind hard times and cold weather. They turned their backs on the decaying industries and cities in northern states, which soon acquired unflattering nicknames like "Frost Belt" and "Rust Belt."

10. **Which statement *best* expresses the main idea of this passage?**

    A. The name and concept of the "Sunbelt" were created by writers in the 1970s.

    B. The quality of life found in northern cities has grown progressively worse over the last 30 years.

    C. The Sunbelt region has experienced rapid population growth, spurred by the many jobs available.

    D. Americans find regions with warm climates preferable to those with colder climates.

11. **According to the information in the passage above, which of the following statements would *most likely* be true?**

    A. Northern industrial cities have seen only moderate growth since World War II.

    B. Southern states' economies have begun to rely less on agriculture in recent decades.

    C. Major cities in the Sunbelt region have experienced more overcrowding than major northern cities.

    D. The Sunbelt's climate was the primary factor in its rapid development.

Directions: *Read the following passage. Then answer questions 12 and 13.*

That slaves, indentured servants, women, Native Americans, and men without land were not protected under the Constitution was forcefully pointed out by historian Charles Beard (1874–1948). In *An Economic Interpretation of the Constitution* (1913) he reviewed the backgrounds of the 55 white men who drew up the Constitution in 1787. Finding most of them to be wealthy landowners, Beard stirred passions pro and con by suggesting that they established a system of government to protect their own economic interests.

12. **Which of the following statements expresses an opinion?**

    A. Slaves, women, and men with no land were not protected under the original Constitution.

    B. The Constitution was written exclusively by white males.

    C. Most of the Constitution's authors were wealthy landowners.

    D. The Constitution created a government that would most benefit the men who wrote it.

13. **With which of the following statements would Charles Beard *most likely* disagree?**

    A. Equal protection for all citizens was a major priority for the writers of the Constitution.

    B. Minority groups were underrepresented among Constitutional delegates.

    C. The writing of the Constitution was greatly influenced by economics.

    D. Constitutional delegates placed a great deal of importance on the protection of citizens' property.

High School Test 3 — Critical Thinking and Reading *(continued)*

Directions: *Read the passage below. Then answer question 14.*

> The reason men enter into society is to protect their property. And the reason they choose a government is to make laws to guard that property.... Certainly society does not want to give the government the power to destroy the very property which it was chosen to protect. Therefore, whenever government tries to take away and destroy the property of the people, or reduce the people to slavery, it puts itself in a state of war with the people. The people are freed from any further obedience to that government... and have the right to establish a new government.
>
> —John Locke, *Two Treatises on Civil Government* (1690)

14. According to John Locke's statements in the passage above, which of the following would he *most likely* support?

    A. a peacekeeping mission in a war-torn country

    B. a mandatory military service requirement for all young men

    C. a revolution against an oppressive dictator

    D. a government seizure of private property

Directions: *Read the following passage. Then answer questions 15 and 16.*

> In December 1828, the Georgia legislature declared the laws of the Cherokee Nation null and void. The Cherokees tried to fight the new state policy in the courts. The case went all the way to the Supreme Court. The Court ruled that only the federal government, not the Georgia legislature, could make laws concerning the Cherokee Nation. Thus, Georgia's laws denying rights to Indians were unconstitutional. Georgia ignored the decision and was supported by President Andrew Jackson.
>
> In May 1830, Congress passed the Indian Removal Act. Under the law, Indians throughout the Southeast had to sign treaties agreeing to move to Indian Territory.
>
> The Creeks, the Choctaws, and the Chickasaws signed removal treaties. Many Cherokees wanted to resist removal. However, in late 1835, the Cherokee Nation, too, surrendered its land east of the Mississippi. In return, Cherokees received $5 million, some land in Indian Territory, and money to pay for the journey west. Thousands of Cherokees never reached their new land in Indian Territory. They died along the route, which the Cherokees called the Trail of Tears.

15. Which of the following was *not* a consequence of the Indian Removal Act?

    A. Native American groups violently resisted removal.

    B. Several Native American leaders signed treaties agreeing to leave their lands in the Southeast.

    C. The authority of the Supreme Court was challenged by Congress.

    D. The Cherokees traveled along the Trail of Tears.

16. Which statement best reflects President Jackson's view of the Indian Removal Act?

    A. He supported a more generous settlement with the Native American groups.

    B. He questioned whether the Indian Removal Act was constitutional.

    C. He favored a plan for settlers and Native Americans to share the land.

    D. He agreed with the Act's removal of Native Americans from the southeastern United States.

High School Test 4 — Communications

Directions: *Read the passage below. Then answer questions 1–4.*

The public's growing disenchantment with Congress and its perception that national legislators are arrogant and dishonest have led to calls for limiting House members to a maximum of six terms and senators to a maximum of two terms (12 years for each). A 1994 Gallup Poll revealed that 80 percent of the American public supported the concept of term limits in some form.

Some critics believe that an American President would be more effective if limited to one six-year term rather than the maximum of two terms (eight years) as stipulated by the Twenty-second Amendment.

Under the Articles of Confederation, representatives were limited in the number of terms they could serve. Although the Framers of the Constitution placed no limits on a representative's terms, they apparently did envision a Congress whose members would serve for a comparatively short period of time. At the Constitutional Convention, Roger Sherman of Connecticut observed that "Representatives ought to return home and mix with the people." The idea of the "citizen legislator" rather than a "career legislator" was the understanding of the Framers. Yet today, well over 90 percent of all House incumbents are reelected. In the Senate, incumbents have averaged a 78 percent reelection rate during the last four decades.

---

1. On the basis of his comment in this passage, if Roger Sherman were alive today, which of the following statements would best explain his position about term limits?

    A. He would think the President should serve an unlimited number of years because he believes the President is a "career legislator."

    B. He would be for term limits because he believes representatives should not spend years in Washington immersed in the political environment.

    C. He would be against term limits because he shares the public's disenchantment with Congress and feels its members are arrogant.

    D. He would be against existing term limits, because he believes members of Congress should stay in office as long as it takes to get work accomplished.

---

2. According to what you have read from this passage, which of the following statements could *best* persuade others against term limits?

    A. It was believed by the Framers of the Constitution that term limits would restrict Congress.

    B. Time has to be spent learning how to handle the presidency as well as preparing for the reelection effort at the end of the first term.

    C. Eighty percent of the Constitutional Congress voted to place term limits on the country's legislators.

    D. Legislators who are aware of the limitation factor would view congressional service as a stepping stone to another career.

3. What is a valid criticism of the Gallup Poll survey that is used as evidence in this passage?

    A. The data from the poll does not support the writer's main point.

    B. The poll data is not related to the writer's topic.

    C. The poll was taken in 1994, and people's attitudes may have changed since then.

    D. The American public's attitudes about term limits are flawed.

High School Test 4 — Communications *(continued)*

4. **You believe that the Framers of the Constitution would have supported term limits. Which statement derived from the passage *best* supports your position?**

    A. Under the Articles of Confederation, representatives were limited in the number of terms they could serve.

    B. The idea of the "citizen legislator" rather than a "career legislator" was the understanding of the Framers.

    C. The Framers of the Constitution placed no limits on a representative's term.

    D. Some critics believe that an American President would be more effective if limited to one six-year term.

Directions: *Read the paragraph and study the population pyramids below. Then answer questions 5–8.*

A population pyramid is a bar graph that shows the percentages of males and females by age group in a particular country. The shape can also tell you whether a population is growing or not. A narrow pyramid base indicates a country's population is declining.

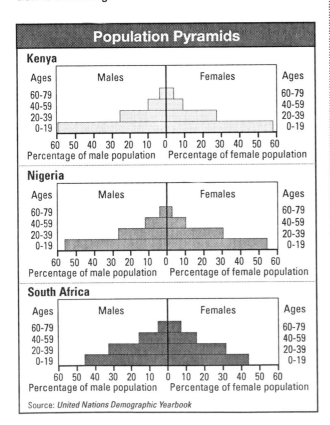

Source: *United Nations Demographic Yearbook*

5. **Which country has the highest percentage of older people in its population, and how do you know this?**

    A. Kenya does because it has the widest base.

    B. Nigeria does because its population bar for ages 0–19 is twice as large as the one for ages 20–39.

    C. South Africa does because its population bar for ages 60–79 is the widest.

    D. Kenya does because it has the biggest difference between the base and the top population bars.

6. **Which of the following statements best explains the information in all three population pyramids?**

    A. Kenya and Nigeria have a higher percentage of young people than South Africa.

    B. South Africa's population is greater than the populations of Kenya and Nigeria combined.

    C. Nigeria has a higher percentage of people ages 60–79 than South Africa or Kenya.

    D. The percentage of males is significantly higher than the percentage of females in Kenya, Nigeria, and South Africa.

High School Test 4 — Communications *(continued)*

7. **In Nigeria's 20–39 population group, there are**
   A. fewer younger men and more older women.
   B. half as many people as there are in the 40–59 group.
   C. twice as many males as there are females.
   D. a higher percentage of females than males.

8. **Which of the following is a valid generalization about these population pyramids?**
   A. Kenya has many more younger people than does South Africa.
   B. The ratio of males to females within each country and within each age group is roughly equivalent.
   C. The younger people are, the lower the life span, regardless of country.
   D. Males outlive females by a ratio of two to one in each country except South Africa.

Directions: *Read the following passage from All Quiet on the Western Front by Erich Maria Remarque. Then answer questions 9–11.*

In the afternoon, about three, he is dead.

I breathe freely again. But only for a short time. Soon the silence is more unbearable than the groans. I wish the gurgling were there again, gasping hoarse, now whistling softly and again hoarse and loud.

It is mad, what I do. But I must do something. I prop the dead man up again so that he lies comfortably, although he feels nothing any more. I close his eyes. They are brown, his hair is black and a bit curly at the sides. . . .

The silence spreads. I talk and must talk. So I speak to him and say to him: Comrade. I did not want to kill you. If you jumped in here again, I would not do it, if you would be sensible too. But you were only an idea to me before, an abstraction that lived in my mind and called forth its appropriate response. It was that abstraction I stabbed. But now, for the first time, I see you are a man like me. I thought of your hand-grenades, of your bayonet, of your rifle; now I see your wife and your face and our fellowship. Forgive me, comrade. We always see too late.

9. **What does the author mean by the statement "We always see too late?"**
   A. Those who act most quickly will be the ones who succeed in this world.
   B. To be on time is the greatest gift one can give to another.
   C. People do things before they stop to think of the results of their actions.
   D. Life is timeless, so it is impossible to achieve everything that must be done.

10. **Which of the following statements supports the narrator's use of the word "comrade" to describe the dead man?**
    A. "I thought of your hand-grenades, of your bayonet, of your rifle. . . ."
    B. ". . . now I see your wife and your face and our fellowship."
    C. "I prop the dead man up again so that he lies comfortably, although he feels nothing any more."
    D. "But you were only an idea to me before, an abstraction that lived in my mind. . . ."

11. **Why is the protagonist in this passage an authority on what has happened?**
    A. He expresses fear that the man will come back to life and haunt him.
    B. He has been wounded by the man's bayonet and hand-grenade, so he has reason to feel this way.
    C. He enjoys the sounds of men dying and thinks he is going mad.
    D. He witnessed the death of the man firsthand.

Name_____ Class_____ Date _____

High School Test 4 — Communications *(continued)*

Directions: *Study the line graphs and table below. Then answer questions 12–14.*

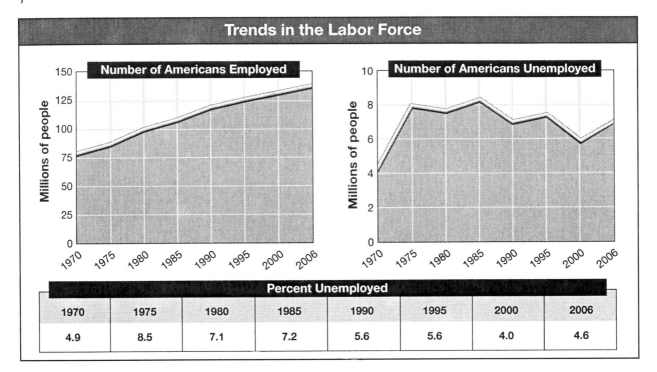

				Percent Unemployed			
1970	1975	1980	1985	1990	1995	2000	2006
4.9	8.5	7.1	7.2	5.6	5.6	4.0	4.6

12. **Which statement *best* summarizes the data shown in the two line graphs and the table?**
   A. Between 1970 and 2006, the number of employed people has steadily risen, whereas the number of unemployed people rose dramatically in the early 1970s, rose again in the 1980s, and then slowly declined until 2006.
   B. Between 1970 and 2006, the changes in employment and unemployment stayed roughly equal, although there was a sharp increase in employment in the early 1970s.
   C. Between 1970 and 2006, the number of unemployed people has decreased in direct proportion to the increase in the number of employed people.
   D. Between 1970 and 2006, the percentage of the population who are employed Americans increased, while the percentage of unemployed non-Americans decreased.

13. **Which of the following statements about these graphs is correct?**
   A. A falling line indicates falling employment levels in both graphs.
   B. The graphs show the percentages of people employed and unemployed, not the actual number.
   C. A rising line indicates rising employment in the graph on the left and rising unemployment in the graph on the right.
   D. Both graphs indicate steady trends over a period of 40 years.

14. **Which of the following would be the best source for the information contained in these graphs?**
   A. the Office of Environmental Management
   B. the Department of Veterans Affairs
   C. the Office of Special Education Programs
   D. the Bureau of Labor Statistics

High School Test 5 — Vocabulary

Americans are estimated to suffer about one billion colds during any given year. While adults average two to four colds per year, children can catch anywhere from six to ten colds in a single year. The <u>fundamental</u> reasons children catch more colds than adults are that they have lower resistance to infections and are around other sick children at school.

Colds occur when people <u>encounter</u> and become infected by one of nearly 200 viruses that can temporarily defeat the human body's defense system. Infection with these viruses will <u>provoke</u> symptoms such as a stuffy nose or a sore throat.

Prevention and treatment remain the best ways to fight the common cold. Health professionals <u>emphasize</u> the importance of washing one's hands frequently to prevent the spread of cold viruses.

1. **All of the following words are antonyms of *fundamental* except for**
   A. nonessential.
   B. basic.
   C. unrelated.
   D. irrelevant.

2. **The word *encounter* could be replaced with which of the following words?**
   A. meet
   B. avoid
   C. give
   D. release

3. **If health professionals *emphasize* the importance of washing one's hands to prevent the spread of cold viruses, it means that they**
   A. want to discourage people from washing their hands too much.
   B. wish to challenge the myth that simply washing hands can prevent colds.
   C. choose to stress the vital role of cleanliness in stopping colds.
   D. decide to warn individuals against needless anxiety about viruses.

4. **A synonym for *provoke* is**
   A. withhold.
   B. cure.
   C. take.
   D. cause.

High School Test 5 — Vocabulary *(continued)*

One of the main advantages of computers is that they allow people to be more <u>efficient</u> at work and at home. In other words, computers can automatically perform many tasks that used to <u>consume</u> people's time. Ironically, most computer users now face a new time-wasting activity: removing unwanted commercial e-mail, or spam, from their electronic mailboxes.

Computer users can take steps to <u>minimize</u> the amount of spam that they receive. For example, a person with an e-mail address should not reveal it in public forums such as Web sites or bulletin boards. As part of this strategy, many people have two different e-mail addresses. They use one e-mail address for public and commercial communications, and <u>restrict</u> the other address to personal messages.

5. **Which of the following words could replace *efficient* in the first paragraph?**

   A. wasteful

   B. intelligent

   C. productive

   D. helpful

6. **Which word in the first paragraph provides a contextual clue that would help to define *consume*?**

   A. mailboxes

   B. advantages

   C. commercial

   D. time-wasting

7. **A synonym for *minimize* is**

   A. reduce.

   B. expand.

   C. control.

   D. enlarge.

8. **According to the passage, an e-mail address that is *restricted* would be**

   A. given out in exchange for money.

   B. used only in certain situations.

   C. never revealed.

   D. changed frequently.

High School Test 5 — Vocabulary *(continued)*

Sharks have a scary reputation, but statistics show the alarm they cause is difficult to <u>justify</u>. Shark attacks are relatively uncommon, and they are rarely fatal. For example, in 2001, there were only 76 unprovoked shark attacks on humans worldwide, resulting in just 5 deaths.

Most shark attacks could be described as "hit-and-runs." What happens is a shark bites and quickly releases a person. It is believed that the shark mistook a person for a fish and then <u>ceases</u> to attack when it realizes its mistake. In most of these cases, the victim <u>sustains</u> injuries to the leg but is otherwise unharmed.

A second, less common, but more dangerous type of attack is the "bump-and-bite." When this occurs, the shark circles and often bumps the victim before attacking. The "bump-and-bite" attack is considered <u>hostile</u> because the shark is either hungry or angry.

9. **Which of the following is a synonym for the word** *cease*?

   A. begin

   B. increase

   C. stop

   D. boost

10. **A phrase that means the same as** *justify* **is**

   A. give reasons for.

   B. get relief from.

   C. suffer under.

   D. weigh the pros and cons of.

11. **A word that means the opposite of** *sustains* **is**

   A. experiences.

   B. suffers.

   C. lacks.

   D. escapes.

12. **Why would a hungry or angry shark attacking a person be thought of as** *hostile*?

   A. The shark is acting in self-defense.

   B. The shark intends to harm the person.

   C. The shark is trying to avoid contact.

   D. The shark seeks to beat its competitors.

High School Test 5 — Vocabulary *(continued)*

A recent exciting <u>prospect</u> in the automobile industry is the hybrid car. Hybrids are cars that run on both gas and electricity, using a system in which a battery and an engine <u>reinforce</u> one another's power. On the one hand, the gas engine helps the vehicle to <u>accelerate</u> from a full stop to driving speed and also charges the battery. In turn, the battery allows the engine to shut off while the car is stopped, but still running. Addi-tionally, the battery provides the automobile with power at speeds below 40 miles per hour.

Hybrid vehicles have several <u>dimensions</u> that make them appealing. First, hybrids get far better gas mileage than most existing cars. Second, hybrids make much less noise because the engine goes quiet every time the vehicle stops at an intersection. Finally, hybrid cars produce less air pollution than regular vehicles.

13. Which phrase could replace "A recent exciting *prospect*"?
   A. A new hot trend
   B. A popular throwback
   C. A nostalgic attitude
   D. A developing style

14. A word that means the opposite of *reinforce* is
   A. enlarge.
   B. support.
   C. argue.
   D. weaken.

15. A way to express the opposite of *accelerate* is
   A. speed up.
   B. increase in velocity.
   C. pick up the pace.
   D. decrease speed.

16. *Dimensions* in this context means "aspects." Which of the following is NOT mentioned in the passage as an appealing aspect of hybrid cars?
   A. Hybrids create less noise pollution.
   B. Hybrids are fun to drive.
   C. Hybrids emit less air pollutants.
   D. Hybrids get fantastic mileage.

High School Test 6 — Writing

Directions: *Read the following passage. Then complete the activity.*

Thanks to advanced technology, people can easily download music from the Internet and obtain even new releases virtually free of charge. People can also copy their friends' CDs and acquire an extensive music collection without spending any money to purchase those CDs themselves.

Some people consider this freedom of access a form of democracy. They believe that sharing music is one form of sharing ideas. They also believe that it helps artists in the long run by making their music available to a wider audience. Other people consider file sharing to be a form of theft. According to the law, the words and music in a musician's songs are his or her property. Musicians earn their living by selling those who are willing to pay access to their songs, usually in the form of a CD. People who obtain a musician's work without paying, according to this argument, are stealing from the musician.

Decide which position you would support: for or against downloading music from the Internet for free. Consider the reasons you would give if you wanted to convince others of your point of view. Then use these reasons to prepare the outline of a persuasive essay.

Use the following form to begin your outline:

I. (major heading)

  A. (subhead)

  (supporting details)

Include at least two major headings in your outline, and as many subheadings and supporting details as you need to explain your viewpoint.

_____

_____

_____

_____

_____

_____

_____

_____

_____

_____

_____

High School Test 6 — Writing *(continued)*

Directions: *Read the passage. Then, in your own words, write a two-sentence summary of the passage.*

Ecotourism is loosely defined as environmentally friendly tourism. As more Americans interest themselves in the environment, ecotourism has emerged as one of the fastest-growing sectors of the travel industry. Americans spend billions of dollars a year traveling to natural areas both in the United States and other countries to view wildlife. Many of these tourists believe that by supporting programs that promise to protect natural areas, they can help improve local economies and the environment at the same time.

Supporters of ecotourism believe that it provides the best way to create jobs and preserve Earth's wild places at the same time. Critics of ecotourism point out that travel to natural areas often has harmful effects. Heavy traffic through natural areas can cause pollution and erosion, damaging land and wildlife. Travelers who are interested in ecotourism should educate themselves first and be sure to find programs and trips that are truly helpful to the environment.

_____

_____

_____

_____

_____

_____

_____

High School Test 6 — Writing *(continued)*

Writers often focus on cause-and-effect relationships in order to illustrate a connection that might not be obvious. Remember, one cause can sometimes have more than one effect. In other cases, an effect happens as a result of more than one cause. And sometimes causes and effects are separated in time; then it can be hard to see how one event caused another.

Directions: *Think of an effect that had more than one cause. Write one or two paragraphs explaining how the effect happened as a result of the factors that caused it. You may draw your topic from something in the news or from your own experiences. Cause-and-effect relationships are often spelled out using words and phrases such as "as a result of," "the reasons for," and "because of."*

_____

_____

_____

_____

_____

_____

_____

_____

_____

_____

_____

_____

_____

_____

_____

_____

_____

_____

_____

_____

_____

_____

_____

_____

_____

High School Test 6 — Writing *(continued)*

The space science community is divided over the issue of a manned mission to Mars. The main point of disagreement is whether this should be a mission for humans or robots. Of course, robots have already landed on Mars and made important discoveries. But, in twenty years, will human astronauts be exploring Mars, or will we still rely on robots?

Supporters of the robots-to-Mars viewpoint argue that sending humans to Mars would be very risky. Perhaps more importantly, it would be incredibly expensive. Machines are relatively cheap, they say, and past experience proves that robots can do the job without putting lives in danger. On the other hand, supporters of human missions say that astronauts could learn more on the spot than machines, simply because humans are more versatile, adaptable, and creative in their research. In addition, humans would be better able to deal with unexpected problems than a robot. Finally, the idea of sending astronauts to Mars is exciting to the general public—probably much more exciting than a robot mission.

Directions: *Imagine you are writing a letter to the editor of your local newspaper supporting one of the two plans for the exploration of Mars: manned missions or robot landers. Remember that in writing a letter to the editor it is usually best to state your views clearly, along with details that support your position. Some possible points you might mention are:*

- the desired goal of space exploration
- the problem or choice faced
- the alternatives available in this situation
- how you chose what you believe is the best alternative

_____

_____

_____

_____

_____

_____

_____

_____

_____

_____

_____

_____

_____

_____

Correlations to Program Resources

Middle Grades Diagnosing Readiness Correlations	Test Items	Civics: Government and Economics in Action
Communications		
Using Reliable Information	3, 9	SE: pp. 5, 119, 132, 275, 284, 302 TE: pp. 275, 408 TR: U3&4, p. 37
Transferring Information from One Medium to Another	2, 8, 11, 12, 13, 14, 16, 18, 19	SE: pp. 12, 24, 36, 76, 216, 231, 296 TE: pp. 76, 100 TR: U1&2, p. 37
Synthesizing Information	5, 7, 15, 17, 18, 20	SE: pp. 131, 134, 182, 262, 288, 366, 370 TE: pp. 370, 384 TR: U5&6, p. 9
Supporting a Position	1, 4, 6, 10, 20	SE: pp. 40, 134, 170, 268, 286, 304, 326, 678 TE: pp. 304, 678
Critical Thinking and Reading		
Identifying Main Ideas/ Summarizing	9	SE: pp. 57, 301, 435, 530, 556, 582 TE: pp. 54, 69, 292, 305, 396, 450, 530, 600 TR: U7–9, pp. 9, 35
Sequencing	6	SE: pp. 162, 171, 227, 234, 280 TE: pp. 348, 350, 358, 363 TR: U3&4, p. 10
Identifying Cause and Effect/Making Predictions	3	SE: pp. 8, 31, 39, 171, 213, 335, 666 TE: pp. 82, 91, 95, 171, 277, 376, 388, 684 TR: U1&2, p. 76, U5&6, p. 48, U7–9, p. 74
Making Inferences/Drawing Conclusions	1, 5, 8, 10, 11	SE: pp. 8, 21, 58, 99, 217, 260, 377 TE: pp. 260, 312 TR: U3&4, p. 24
Making Valid Generalizations	12	SE: pp. 33, 44, 67, 262, 288, 334 TR: U5&6, p. 22

SE: Student Edition • TE: Teacher's Edition • TR: Teaching Resources • U: Unit Booklet

Correlations to Program Resources

Middle Grades Diagnosing Readiness Correlations (continued)	Test Items	Civics: Government and Economics in Action
Critical Thinking and Reading (continued)		
Distinguishing Fact and Opinion	16	SE: pp. 342, 362, 568 TE: pp. 342, 362 TR: U3&4, p. 65
Comparing and Contrasting	7, 14	SE: pp. 222, 228, 259, 303, 309, 325, 610 TE: pp. 132, 191, 210, 223, 318, 327, 336, 610 TR: U7–9, p. 48
Analyzing Primary and Secondary Sources	2, 4	SE: pp. 104, 119, 132, 221, 431, 504, 568 TE: pp. 132, 191 TR: U1&2, p. 63
Recognizing Bias and Propaganda	16	SE: pp. 104, 387, 490, 506, 541, 665 TE: pp. 490, 541, 568, 626 TR: U5&6, p. 74, U7–9, p. 22
Identifying Frame of Reference and Point of View	13	SE: pp. 50, 297, 362, 503, 627, 688 TE: pp. 50, 66, 119, 362 TR: U1&2, p. 23
Decision Making	15	SE: pp. 180, 408, 421, 551, 638 TE: p. 638 TR: U7–9, p. 61
Problem Solving	15	SE: pp. 387, 396, 407, 424, 449, 476 TE: pp. 476, 521 TR: U5&6, p. 61
Geographic Literacy		
Using the Cartographer's Tools	4, 5, 6, 7, 8, 10, 11, 12, 13, 15, 16	SE: pp. 86, 189, 273, 296, 314, 674, 675, 692 TE: pp. 314, 692 TR: U3&4, p. 51, U7–9, p. 87

SE: Student Edition • TE: Teacher's Edition • TR: Teaching Resources • U: Unit Booklet

Correlations to Program Resources

Middle Grades Diagnosing Readiness Correlations (continued)	Test Items	Civics: Government and Economics in Action
Geographic Literacy (continued)		
Analyzing and Interpreting Special Purpose Maps	1, 2, 3, 9, 14, 17	SE: pp. 86, 189, 273, 296, 314, 674, 675, 692 TE: pp. 314, 692 TR: U3&4, p. 51, U7–9, p. 87
Visual Analysis		
Analyzing Graphic Data	1, 2, 3, 4, 5	SE: pp. 6, 24, 26, 71, 93, 252 TE: pp. 6, 24, 38 TR: U1&2, p. 9
Analyzing Images	6, 7, 8, 9, 10	SE: pp. 20, 47, 65, 90, 166, 195, 325 TE: pp. 90, 166, 195, 224 TR: U1&2, pp. 50, 88
Vocabulary Development		
Using Social Studies Terms Correctly	1, 2, 3, 4, 5, 6, 7, 8, 9, 10, 11, 12, 13, 14, 15, 16	SE: Chapter Reviews TR: Chapter Vocabulary Practice pages
Writing Development		
Supporting a Position	Writing Test, p. 36	SE: pp. 40, 134, 170, 268, 286, 304, 326, 678 TE: pp. 304, 678
Comparing and Contrasting	Writing Test, p. 37	SE: pp. 222, 228, 259, 303, 309, 325, 610 TE: pp. 132, 191, 210, 223, 318, 327, 336, 610 TR: U7–9, p. 48
Identifying Main Ideas	Writing Test, p. 38	SE: pp. 57, 301, 435, 530, 556, 582 TE: pp. 54, 69, 292, 305, 396, 450, 530, 600 TR: U7–9, pp. 9, 35
Summarizing	Writing Test, p. 39	SE: pp. 57, 301, 435, 530, 556, 582 TE: pp. 54, 69, 292, 305, 396, 450, 530, 600 TR: U7–9, pp. 9, 35

SE: Student Edition • TE: Teacher's Edition • TR: Teaching Resources • U: Unit Booklet

Correlations to Program Resources

High School Diagnosing Readiness Correlations	Test Items	Civics: Government and Economics in Action
Communications		
Using Reliable Information	3, 11, 14	SE: pp. 5, 119, 132, 275, 284, 302 TE: pp. 275, 408 TR: U3&4, p. 37
Transferring Information from One Medium to Another	7, 8, 12	SE: pp. 12, 24, 36, 76, 216, 231, 296 TE: pp. 76, 100 TR: U1&2, p. 37
Synthesizing Information	5, 6, 9, 12, 13	SE: pp. 131, 134, 182, 262, 288, 366, 370 TE: pp. 370, 384 TR: U5&6, p. 9
Supporting a Position	1, 2, 4, 10	SE: pp. 40, 134, 170, 268, 286, 304, 326, 678 TE: pp. 304, 678
Critical Thinking and Reading		
Identifying Main Ideas/ Summarizing	4, 10	SE: pp. 57, 301, 435, 530, 556, 582 TE: pp. 54, 69, 292, 305, 396, 450, 530, 600 TR: U7–9, pp. 9, 35
Sequencing	8	SE: pp. 162, 171, 227, 234, 280 TE: pp. 348, 350, 358, 363 TR: U3&4, p. 10
Identifying Cause and Effect/Making Predictions	15	SE: pp. 8, 31, 39, 171, 213, 335, 666 TE: pp. 82, 91, 95, 171, 277, 376, 388, 684 TR: U1&2, p. 76, U5&6, p. 48, U7–9, p. 74

SE: Student Edition • TE: Teacher's Edition • TR: Teaching Resources • U: Unit Booklet

Correlations to Program Resources

High School Diagnosing Readiness Correlations (continued)	Test Items	Civics: Government and Economics in Action
Critical Thinking and Reading (continued)		
Making Inferences/Drawing Conclusions	14, 16	SE: pp. 8, 21, 58, 99, 217, 260, 377 TE: pp. 260, 312 TR: U3&4, p. 24
Making Valid Generalizations	1, 11	SE: pp. 33, 44, 67, 262, 288, 334 TR: U5&6, p. 22
Distinguishing Fact and Opinion	3, 12	SE: pp. 342, 362, 568 TE: pp. 342, 362 TR: U3&4, p. 65
Comparing and Contrasting	2	SE: pp. 222, 228, 259, 303, 309, 325, 610 TE: pp. 132, 191, 210, 223, 318, 327, 336, 610 TR: U7–9, p. 48
Analyzing Primary and Secondary Sources	5	SE: pp. 104, 119, 132, 221, 431, 504, 568 TE: pp. 132, 191 TR: U1&2, p. 63
Recognizing Bias and Propaganda	6	SE: pp. 104, 387, 490, 506, 541, 665 TE: pp. 490, 541, 568, 626 TR: U5&6, p. 74, U7–9, p. 22
Identifying Frame of Reference and Point of View	9, 13	SE: pp. 50, 297, 362, 503, 627, 688 TE: pp. 50, 66, 119, 362 TR: U1&2, p. 23
Decision Making		SE: pp. 180, 408, 421, 551, 638 TE: p. 638 TR: U7–9, p. 61

SE: Student Edition • TE: Teacher's Edition • TR: Teaching Resources • U: Unit Booklet

Correlations to Program Resources

High School Diagnosing Readiness Correlations (continued)	Test Items	Civics: Government and Economics in Action
Critical Thinking and Reading (continued)		
Problem Solving	7	SE: pp. 387, 396, 407, 424, 449, 476 TE: pp. 476, 521 TR: U5&6, p. 61
Geographic Literacy		
Using the Cartographer's Tools	1, 3, 4, 5, 7, 9, 10, 11, 12	SE: pp. 86, 189, 273, 296, 314, 674, 675, 692 TE: pp. 314, 692 TR: U3&4, p. 51, U7–9, p. 87
Analyzing and Interpreting Special Purpose Maps	2, 6, 8, 13, 14, 15, 16, 17, 18	SE: pp. 86, 189, 273, 296, 314, 674, 675, 692 TE: pp. 314, 692 TR: U3&4, p. 51, U7–9, p. 87
Visual Analysis		
Analyzing Graphic Data	5, 6, 7	SE: pp. 6, 24, 26, 71, 93, 252 TE: pp. 6, 24, 38 TR: U1&2, p. 9
Analyzing Images	1, 2, 3, 4	SE: pp. 20, 47, 65, 90, 166, 195, 325 TE: pp. 90, 166, 195, 224 TR: U1&2, pp. 50, 88
Vocabulary Development		
Using Social Studies Terms Correctly	1, 2, 3, 4, 5, 6, 7, 8, 9, 10, 11, 12, 13, 14, 15, 16	SE: Chapter Reviews TR: Chapter Vocabulary Practice pages

SE: Student Edition • TE: Teacher's Edition • TR: Teaching Resources • U: Unit Booklet

Correlations to Program Resources

High School Diagnosing Readiness Correlations (continued)	Test Items	Civics: Government and Economics in Action
Writing Development		
Identifying Frame of Reference and Point of View	Writing Test, p. 59	SE: pp. 50, 297, 362, 503, 627, 688 TE: pp. 50, 66, 119, 362 TR: U1&2, p. 23
Summarizing	Writing Test, p. 60	SE: pp. 57, 301, 435, 530, 556, 582 TE: pp. 54, 69, 292, 305, 396, 450, 530, 600 TR: U7–9, pp. 9, 35
Identifying Cause and Effect	Writing Test, p. 61	SE: pp. 31, 39, 171 TE: pp. 82, 91, 95, 171, 277, 376, 388 TR: U1&2, p. 76, U5&6, p. 48
Supporting a Position	Writing Test, p. 62	SE: pp. 40, 134, 170, 268, 286, 304, 326, 678 TE: pp. 304, 678

SE: Student Edition • TE: Teacher's Edition • TR: Teaching Resources • U: Unit Booklet

National Standards for Civics and Government

9–12 Content Standards

I. **What are Civic Life, Politics, and Government?**

A. What is civic life? What is politics? What is government? Why are government and politics necessary? What purposes should government serve?

B. What are the essential characteristics of limited and unlimited government?

C. What are the nature and purposes of constitutions?

D. What are alternative ways of organizing constitutional governments?

II. **What are the Foundations of the American Political System?**

A. What is the American idea of constitutional government?

B. What are the distinctive characteristics of American society?

C. What is American political culture?

D. What values and principles are basic to American constitutional democracy?

III. **How Does the Government Established by the Constitution Embody the Purposes, Values, and Principles of American Democracy?**

A. How are power and responsibility distributed, shared, and limited in the government established by the United States Constitution?

B. How is the national government organized and what does it do?

C. How are state and local governments organized and what do they do?

D. What is the place of law in the American constitutional system?

E. How does the American political system provide for choice and opportunities for participation?

IV. **What is the Relationship of the United States to Other Nations and to World Affairs?**

A. How is the world organized politically?

B. How do the domestic politics and constitutional principles of the United States affect its relations with the world?

C. How has the United States influenced other nations, and how have other nations influenced American politics and society?

V. **What are the Roles of the Citizen in American Democracy?**

A. What is citizenship?

B. What are the rights of citizens?

C. What are the responsibilities of citizens?

D. What civic dispositions or traits of private and public character are important to the preservation and improvement of American constitutional democracy?

E. How can citizens take part in civic life?

Benchmark Tests

Test 1

Directions: *Each question is followed by four choices. Identify the letter of the choice that best completes the statement or answers the question.*

1. **Which are the five largest ethnic groups in American society?**
   A. Spanish American, English American, Hispanic American, Asian American, Latino American
   B. African American, European American, Hispanic American, Asian American, Native American
   C. African American, German American, Hispanic American, Asian American, Native American
   D. African American, Eurasian, Hispanic American, Irish American, Native American

2. **Suki was born in Japan. Her parents are Japanese citizens. Her family moved to Texas five years ago. She has a good moral character and is loyal to the principles of the U.S. Constitution. She can read, write, and speak English well, and she has a solid knowledge of history and government. What other requirement must Suki meet before she can become a U.S. citizen?**
   A. At least one of her parents must be a U.S. citizen.
   B. She must be fingerprinted by the FBI.
   C. She must have worked in the country for at least a year.
   D. She must be at least 18 years old.

3. **Which one of the following actions is NOT voluntary for American citizens?**
   A. voting
   B. obeying the laws
   C. influencing government actions
   D. running for office

4. **Why is the size of the typical American family shrinking?**
   A. Divorce is more common.
   B. More unmarried mothers are choosing to raise their children alone.
   C. There are more blended families today.
   D. On average, couples are having fewer children.

5. **One hundred years ago, most Americans worked in farming and manufacturing. What word or phrase best describes the jobs that most Americans hold today?**
   A. hospitality
   B. health care
   C. high technology
   D. service

6. **Each of the following is a part of socialization *except***
   A. meeting the needs of everyone in a group.
   B. learning how to participate in a group.
   C. accepting the values of a group.
   D. learning the rules for behavior within a group.

7. **Which two rights must Americans frequently balance when they debate religious values?**
   A. freedom of speech and freedom of the press
   B. freedom to peacefully organize and freedom of speech
   C. freedom of religion and freedom of speech
   D. freedom of religion and freedom to peacefully organize

8. **One of the basic rights of an American citizen is the right to a fair trial. Who serves on a jury to determine a person's guilt or innocence "beyond a reasonable doubt"?**
   A. members of Congress
   B. citizens
   C. judges
   D. witnesses

9. **Julian's father serves on the board of education in his school district. Next year he will help campaign for a candidate running for city commissioner. What is Julian's father's social role?**
   A. social group member
   B. citizen
   C. worker/student
   D. consumer

10. **All of the following are duties of citizens except**
    A. serving on juries.
    B. paying taxes.
    C. defending the nation.
    D. attending religious services.

11. **What does diversity mean?**
    A. fairness
    B. cultural awareness
    C. differences
    D. opportunity

12. **Complete this analogy. North Korea : dictatorship :: United States : _____**
    A. king
    B. democracy
    C. president
    D. monarchy

13. **All of the following are reasons why the population of older Americans is increasing more rapidly than other age groups except**
    A. adults of child-bearing age are having fewer children.
    B. medical care is improving so people are living longer.
    C. the "baby boomer" group is aging.
    D. the death rate of people 20 and younger is increasing.

14. **In the United States, _____ are allowed to influence government by expressing their opinions and by voting.**
    A. all citizens
    B. only members of Congress
    C. all residents, including aliens
    D. only members of the armed forces

15. **In a constitutional monarchy, a monarch performs ceremonial duties, but real power is held by**
    A. elected representatives.
    B. a single person who takes power by force.
    C. a council of military leaders.
    D. a foreign invader.

16. **What is the process of learning what is correct and incorrect political behavior?**

    A. patriotism

    B. diversification

    C. equal opportunity

    D. political socialization

17. **Which of the following is a role of government in the United States?**

    A. imposing a national religion

    B. protecting the country against outside attack

    C. deciding what goods citizens should buy

    D. ensuring that no citizens are poor

18. **For U.S. citizens, paying taxes and obeying the law are**

    A. privileges.

    B. rights.

    C. duties.

    D. freedoms.

19. **In our economic system, the prices of goods and services are usually determined by**

    A. Congressional legislation and enforced by the executive branch.

    B. the seller, who can charge whatever he or she thinks people will pay.

    C. traditional prices, which remain steady over time.

    D. individual cities and communities and enforced by local authorities.

20. **The type of government in which power is held by one individual and that power is hereditary is a**

    A. dictatorship.

    B. aristocracy.

    C. monarchy.

    D. democracy.

Benchmark Tests

Test 2

Directions: *Each question is followed by four choices. Identify the letter of the choice that best completes the statement or answers the question.*

1. **How do the principles of federalism, separation of powers, and checks and balances affect the government?**
   A. They give the government more power with foreign nations.
   B. They ensure that the rights of states are protected.
   C. They guarantee that changes to the constitution are made only by the will of the people.
   D. They limit the government's power.

2. **Which freedom for students did the Supreme Court uphold in the Tinker case in 1965?**
   A. freedom of press
   B. freedom of speech
   C. freedom of assembly
   D. freedom from search and seizure

3. **Study the checks and balances chart. If the President thinks an action taken by Congress is not in the people's best interest, what action can he or she take?**
   A. The President may appoint federal judges.
   B. The President may override a presidential veto.
   C. The President may veto acts of Congress.
   D. The President may impeach federal judges.

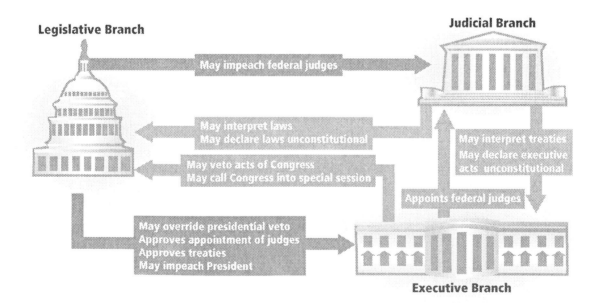

Legislative Branch

Judicial Branch

May impeach federal judges

May interpret laws
May declare laws unconstitutional

May veto acts of Congress
May call Congress into special session

May interpret treaties
May declare executive acts unconstitutional

Appoints federal judges

May override presidential veto
Approves appointment of judges
Approves treaties
May impeach President

Executive Branch

4. **Which case illustrates the notion that freedom of speech and assembly for all, not only for those who agree with us, is a First Amendment right?**

   A. the Tinker case

   B. *Brown* v. *Board of Education of Topeka*

   C. *Plessy* v. *Ferguson*

   D. the Skokie case

5. **How might a Supreme Court decision be overturned by a later Court decision?**

   A. The President convinces members of the Court that their decision was biased and unfair.

   B. Congress decides that at least one member of the Court was incompetent at the time of the decision.

   C. A referendum is presented to the voters, who decide that the Court made a wrong decision.

   D. New evidence or new ideas are presented that lead the Court to change an earlier Court's interpretation.

6. **Which set of words *best* completes the following sentence? Although colonists had the right to elect members of their _____ , they still were subject to the authority of _____ , who established each colony through a _____ .**

   A. Congress, the President, formal decree

   B. legislature, England, proprietor

   C. colony, citizens, charter

   D. legislature, England, charter

7. **What was Roger Sherman's Great Compromise concerning the House and the Senate?**

   A. Members of the House would be elected by the people, and senators would be elected by members of the House.

   B. Members of the House would be elected by the people, and senators would be appointed by the President.

   C. Members of the House would be elected on the basis of state population, and each state would have two senators, regardless of its population.

   D. Members of both the House and the Senate would be elected on the basis of state population.

8. **Tamika will celebrate her eighteenth birthday next month. What right will she then have that is guaranteed by a Constitutional amendment?**

   A. the right to pay income tax

   B. the right to serve on a jury

   C. the right to vote

   D. the right to marry

9. **Which of the following statements *best* describes why the right to bear arms was added to the Bill of Rights in 1791?**

   A. Many delegates felt it provided important protection against abuses of government power.

   B. Many delegates believed that only members of the Continental Army had the right to bear arms.

   C. Many delegates felt that owning a gun was the only way to provide protection from hostile neighbors.

   D. Many delegates wanted their gun collections protected from the federal government.

10. The girl in the photograph is exercising what right, based on a principle argued in _Phillips_ v. _Martin Marietta Corporation_?

A. the right to equal protection under the law

B. the right to hold elected office

C. the right to vote

D. the right to a fair trial

11. I support the Constitution because individual states cannot safely protect themselves against foreign nations. I believe the Constitution will help regulate trade in our nation. The Constitution makes sure that my American money keeps its value both here and in other countries. Who am I?

A. a Whig

B. a Federalist

C. a Tory

D. a Loyalist

12. Choose the words that _best_ complete this sentence: Amendments to the Constitution are usually approved first by _____ and then proposed to _____.

A. Congress, the states

B. the states, Congress

C. the President, Congress

D. the executive branch, the judicial branch

13. What does the phrase "No taxation without representation" mean?

A. The colonists did not want to pay taxes unless the taxes represented a percentage of their income.

B. The colonists refused to pay taxes on tea that arrived in the colonies from Great Britain.

C. The colonists did not want to pay taxes because they had no one representing them in Parliament.

D. Representatives in the legislature did not have to pay taxes on the money they earned working for the people.

14. How did the Supreme Court justify its decision that, according to the Constitution, Dred Scott was not a free man?

A. The Court said that because Scott's permanent residence was in Alabama, a slave state, he was not free to travel with his owner.

B. The Court said that Scott's owner had filed the appropriate paperwork listing Scott as a slave for the next seven years.

C. The Court said that slaves were property and Congress could not prevent owners from taking slaves where they wished.

D. The Court said that Scott had not properly bought his freedom from his owner.

15. Complete this analogy. United States :
citizens :: England : ___ ____
   A. subjects
   B. legislators
   C. laypeople
   D. people

16. A constitution is a
   A. collection of amendments.
   B. history of court decisions.
   C. agreement between countries.
   D. plan of government.

17. What is the purpose of the Preamble of the U.S. Constitution?
   A. It states the goals of the new government.
   B. It declares independence from Great Britain.
   C. It divides government into three branches.
   D. It describes how the Constitution can be amended.

18. The U.S. Constitution replaced the Articles of Confederation. What was the basic problem with the Articles of Confederation?
   A. It created a national government that was too weak.
   B. It gave too much power to the large states.
   C. It created a national government that was too strong.
   D. It was never ratified.

19. Three main principles of the U.S. Constitution are federalism, separation of powers, and checks and balances. Together, these three principles contribute to
   A. a limited government.
   B. direct democracy.
   C. an unlimited government.
   D. the creation of an executive branch.

20. The overall purpose of the Bill of Rights was to
   A. create a stronger central government.
   B. describe citizens' basic rights so that they could be protected.
   C. increase the power of the legislative branch.
   D. eliminate the "necessary and proper" clause.

Benchmark Tests

Test 3

Directions: *Each question is followed by four choices. Identify the letter of the choice that best completes the statement or answers the question.*

1. **Why have states in the deep South generally had more constitutions than other states?**
   A. New constitutions were written when the South changed from an industrial to a rural economic base.
   B. New constitutions were written after the California gold rush, when the states gained new wealth.
   C. New constitutions were written after these states seceded from the Union and again after the Civil War.
   D. New constitutions were written after the American Revolution to help establish trade with the British.

2. **While the President is free to choose anyone to head an executive department, what constitutional rule can provide a check on this power?**
   A. Executive departments have more than one leader, so no single person has too much power.
   B. Appointments must be approved by the Vice President.
   C. Appointments must be approved by the Senate.
   D. The head of the department is free to select his or her own staff.

3. **Why did the framers of the Constitution limit the term of the President?**
   A. They thought it was only fair to allow as many people as possible to have a chance to become President.
   B. They thought that the longer the President was in office, the more likely he or she would be subject to an assassination attempt.
   C. They thought it would be too much of a burden on one person to serve for an extended period of time.
   D. They had experience with the tyranny of a king, and they wanted to make sure that the President would only serve a limited term.

4. **If the city of Baltimore, Maryland, received money from the federal and state governments to begin job training programs for residents, who would carry out these programs?**
   A. the federal government
   B. the local government in Baltimore
   C. the federal and state governments
   D. the Maryland state government

5. Jack lives in one of the biggest lumber-producing towns in the West. He thought his father, as a new member of Congress, would be able to cast his votes based only on the needs of people in their town. Why might Jack be wrong?

   A. Congress deals only with national issues, not matters that affect people on a local level.

   B. Jack's father has a responsibility to vote for what is best for the whole nation, not just for what will please his constituents.

   C. Jack's father will not be allowed to vote on matters related to the needs of his constituents because if would be a conflict of interest.

   D. His father's vote will not count as much as the votes of veteran members of Congress because he is a new member.

6. Read the cartoon. What is the message the cartoonist is trying to convey?

   A. Aliens would find our system of government funny.

   B. We have different levels of government in our political system, each with its own powers.

   C. We have a President who governs us at the local, county, state, and federal levels.

   D. The U.S. Constitution establishes four branches of government: local, county, state, and federal.

7. What does the War Powers Resolution state?

   A. The President does not have the power to send troops to a foreign country without congressional approval.

   B. The Secretary of State is in charge of the armed forces, so the President cannot make foreign policy decisions.

   C. If the President sends American troops to a foreign country, they may not stay there for more than 60 days without congressional approval.

   D. The Supreme Court must review whether sending troops to a foreign country is constitutional.

8. Whose responsibility is it to review laws, consider precedents, determine lawmakers' intentions, and remain impartial?

   A. judges

   B. senators

   C. the President

   D. attorneys

9. Complete this analogy. Leader of the federal executive branch : _____ :: Leader of a state's executive branch : _____

   A. President; governor

   B. President; senator

   C. chief executive; President

   D. Commander in Chief; Lieutenant Governor

10. What is the *best* reason given for choosing judges through a governor's appointments instead of through state elections?

A. Governors should select judges because they, not the voters, know who is best for these jobs.

B. Judges should make decisions based on the law and facts, not on what might please voters in an election.

C. Judges should be selected based on merit after taking a Civil Service exam to prove their fitness for the position.

D. Allowing governors to appoint judges would create a system of checks and balances.

11. My committee is permanent. Because we control the fate of bills, my committee has a lot of power. First, we study a bill and then we hold hearings. Next, my committee decides whether to recommend that the entire Senate vote on the bill. If we do not recommend a bill, it dies. Which kind of committee do I lead?

A. standing

B. select

C. joint

D. conference

12. In which situation is an appeals court *most likely* to hear a case?

A. All parties have argued their case before a judge but NOT before a jury.

B. The plaintiff or defendant believes the decision made in the original court was unfair.

C. All parties agree on the judge or jury's decision.

D. The defendant is sentenced by the lower court and fined by the judge.

13. Which category best describes these jobs: sheriff, commissioner, board, assessor, and treasurer?

A. jobs for people who work in Congress

B. jobs for people who work in the judicial branch of government

C. jobs for people who work for the school board

D. jobs for people who work in county government

14. A state's population determines how many members it sends to the House of Representatives. According to the Constitution, how is this count made?

A. by a popular vote every other year

B. by a census every ten years

C. by a census every five years

D. by an election every four years

15. **Look at the political cartoon. What does the cartoonist say about how some citizens feel about financing public services with their tax dollars?**
    A. Citizens would happily pay if the local government would hire skilled people to do these jobs.
    B. Citizens favor programs that improve areas such as schools and the environment but do not always want to pay taxes for them.
    C. Citizens are not in favor of local funding and oppose local improvement programs, regardless of who pays the bill.
    D. Citizens often volunteer to help institutions like schools and the environment.

16. **Which category includes all of these items: house of representatives, assembly, general assembly, and house of delegates?**
    A. governors' offices
    B. state legislatures
    C. the federal government
    D. state districts

17. **To whom does the Constitution give the following powers: regulate commerce to promote general welfare, collect taxes and borrow money, establish and maintain an army, and decide how money is spent?**
    A. the President
    B. the Supreme Court
    C. Congress
    D. the states

18. **When Laura's father served as a Senator, Laura worried every few years that her father might lose his job in an election. What is different now that her father is a Supreme Court justice?**
    A. Supreme Court justices are subject to the President, who can fire them at any time.
    B. The president pro tem of the Senate may remove Laura's father with the agreement of the Secretary of State.
    C. If the political party in control of the Senate changes hands, Laura's father might have to resign.
    D. Laura's father has a life term and can be removed only through impeachment.

19. In cases dealing with individual rights, why is it sometimes unclear whether the federal Constitution or a state constitution applies?

A. State constitutions are open to interpretation, but the federal Constitution is not.

B. Separate judges review the federal and state constitutions, so they come to different conclusions.

C. Some state constitutions offer greater rights and freedoms than the federal Constitution.

D. Individual rights are the federal courts' specialty, and lower courts usually do not handle these matters.

20. Complete this analogy. House of Representatives : Speaker of the House :: Senate : _____

A. Speaker of the Senate

B. Whip

C. Leader of the Senate

D. Vice President

Benchmark Tests

Test 4

Directions: *Each question is followed by four choices. Identify the letter of the choice that best completes the statement or answers the question.*

1. **What explains the increase in union membership after 1930?**
   A. Congress passed the National Labor Relations Act requiring employers to bargain with unions.
   B. Congress passed the Taft-Hartley Act putting limits on the powers of unions and union leaders.
   C. Industrial unions lost favor with Americans because they threatened workers' wages.
   D. Because the AFL and the CIO were rival unions, membership rose as workers joined in the fight for better representation.

2. **According to this map, which city is home to the Fourth District Federal Reserve Bank?**
   A. New York
   B. Atlanta
   C. Cleveland
   D. Richmond

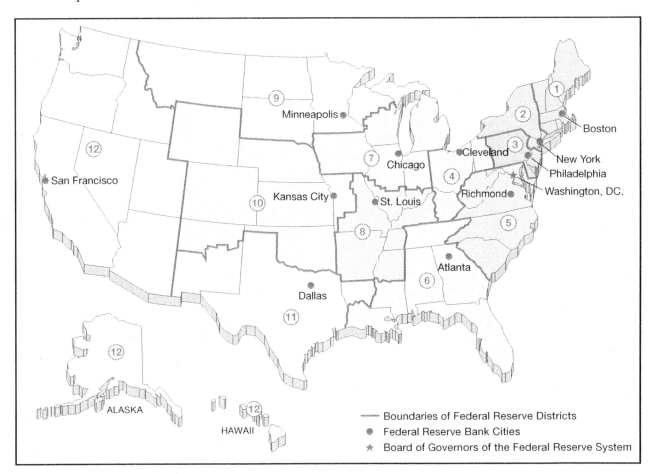

- ——— Boundaries of Federal Reserve Districts
- ● Federal Reserve Bank Cities
- ★ Board of Governors of the Federal Reserve System

3. **Why should the size of the national debt be a concern to all Americans?**
   A. The debt threatens the government's ability to pay for programs and manage the economy.
   B. If the national debt is paid too quickly, creditors may force interest rates to rise.
   C. The debt means that Congress will have to enact new laws to limit private spending, particularly on high technology products and automobiles.
   D. If the size of the debt rises even a little, the government will need to eliminate excise taxes and raise income taxes.

4. **Mrs. Thompson's gift shop was destroyed by an arsonist. Which type of insurance would provide coverage in this case?**
   A. life
   B. property
   C. liability
   D. bankruptcy

5. **Why is scarcity a problem both for rich and poor societies?**
   A. Resources are never common and rarely fulfill needs in any society.
   B. Scarcity is based on the relationship between wants and the resources available to satisfy them, and these are factors in every society.
   C. Wants are influenced by the society in which we live, and cultural differences will always exist.
   D. People's wants frequently change, so having the right resources in the amounts needed is rare.

6. **Which is NOT a characteristic of currency?**
   A. It can be counted and measured.
   B. It is not easily destroyed.
   C. It is easy to carry and use.
   D. It is accepted everywhere.

7. **Supply and demand are determined by**
   A. the decisions of the legislature in each state or district.
   B. the actions of economists working at the stock exchange.
   C. the choices people make when they shop in a market economy.
   D. what happens when people decide to export goods and services.

8. **Andre wants to start a baked goods business, and as a member of the economic community he must first decide what and how much to produce. In making this decision, he will consider all of the following factors** *except*
   A. how much and what type of baked goods people will want to eat.
   B. how the ovens and kitchen equipment should be acquired.
   C. how much of each ingredient he will need and the size of his oven.
   D. how many employees he will need to hire to bake a certain amount of product.

9. **Cara earns $25,000 a year plus fringe benefits as a sales associate. Beth works for herself as a business consultant, earning $29,000, but she has no fringe benefits. Why might Beth be envious of Cara's position, even though Beth earns more per year?**
   A. Fringe benefits are bonuses paid to employees at the end of the year, so Cara can expect to earn far more than $25,000.
   B. Cara's fringe benefits mean that she'll earn a commission on each item she sells, whereas Beth is on a fixed income.
   C. Fringe benefits, such as medical care and sick leave, mean that Cara does not need to set aside part of her income for these purposes.
   D. Beth has no job security, while Cara will be able to keep her job indefinitely.

10. **Who controls production in a command society?**

   A. the government

   B. private individuals

   C. monopolies

   D. voters

11. **What does this 1884 cartoon say about the Standard Oil Company?**

   A. Standard Oil Company is like a big barrel of snakes that is outsmarting its competitors.

   B. Standard Oil Company is known for filing antitrust suits against small businesses in the marketplace.

   C. Standard Oil Company shares its profits with its employees.

   D. Standard Oil Company has taken hold of the oil industry with its "tentacles."

12. **Which is NOT a basic characteristic of a traditional economy?**

   A. Decisions are based on long-standing customs.

   B. Jobs are passed down from generation to generation.

   C. Change occurs slowly, if at all.

   D. Individual freedom is considered very important.

13. **The owner has the freedom to decide how to run the business, all profits belong to the owner, and the owner has the responsibility for paying off loans. What is this type of business called?**

   A. individual ownership

   B. limited partnership

   C. individual corporation

   D. sole proprietorship

14. **Claire's father owns a restaurant. She says her father makes all the rules of his business. However, her friend Jeremiah argues that Claire's father has to follow laws established by the government, too. Who is right, and why?**

   A. Claire is right because as owner of the restaurant, her father can make any rules he chooses.

   B. Jeremiah is right because governments set rules, such as those for safety and working conditions, that regulate business practices.

   C. Jeremiah is right because governments want to limit free enterprise and control the markets, particularly in the food industry.

   D. Claire is right because restaurants are regulated by the Food and Drug Administration, not the federal government.

15. **A group of several companies that work together and agree to charge high prices is called a**
    A. trust.
    B. monopoly.
    C. business cycle.
    D. deficit spender.

16. **In 2004, the federal budget was more than**
    A. $20 million.
    B. $200 million.
    C. $2 billion.
    D. $2 trillion.

17. **What is one of the functions of the Federal Reserve Bank?**
    A. enforcing regulations on the banking industry
    B. providing individual checking accounts
    C. setting the minimum wage
    D. protecting the environment

18. **Personal income tax is based on a percentage of income. As an individual's income increases, which of the following is most likely to happen?**
    A. The amount of money he or she pays in income tax will stay the same.
    B. The percentage of his or her income paid as income tax will increase.
    C. The amount of money he or she pays in income tax will decrease.
    D. The percentage of his or her income paid as income tax will decrease.

19. **The writers of the U.S. Constitution believed that the United States should have an economy based on**
    A. a barter system.
    B. full employment.
    C. a market system.
    D. a high degree of government control.

20. **As the economy became more industrialized in the 1800s, thousands of former craftspeople, farmhands, and new immigrants**
    A. became wage laborers.
    B. ran up high credit card debt.
    C. emigrated to Europe.
    D. formed corporations.

Benchmark Tests

Test 5

Directions: *Each question is followed by four choices. Identify the letter of the choice that best completes the statement or answers the question.*

1. **Why would a defendant accept a plea bargain rather than the alternative?**
   A. The defendant's trial will not be shown on television or covered in the local newspapers.
   B. The defendant probably will receive a milder punishment with a plea bargain than with a trial.
   C. The defendant will be able to take an active role in the jury selection at the trial and be present during all proceedings.
   D. The defendant will get a stronger punishment with a plea bargain, but the conviction will not appear on his or her permanent record.

2. **Domestic relations cases include all of the following** *except*
   A. compensation for breach of contract.
   B. divorce.
   C. property divisions.
   D. custody.

3. **Read the following excerpt from a campaign speech: "As mayor of your town, I will fight for laws that protect the safety, property, and freedoms of each individual and our society as a whole." Which of the following** *best* **describes the candidate's main position?**
   A. He pledges to promote the general welfare of all people.
   B. He wants to break some environmental laws in order to promote the common good.
   C. He will eliminate laws that protect safety, property, and individual freedoms.
   D. He wants to promote the common good of all his constituents.

4. **Fifteen-year-old Simone has been caught skipping school at least once a month, and last year, she ran away from home twice. She has been judged to be beyond the control of her parents. What is the term the juvenile justice system uses to describe children like Simone?**
   A. criminals
   B. delinquents
   C. disobedient
   D. status offenders

5. **Complete this analogy. Civil law : settles disagreements :: Criminal law :**
   _____
   A. determines guilt or innocence
   B. levies fines
   C. settles lawsuits
   D. evaluates appeals

Name_____ Class_____ Date _____

6. Which type of case does a grand jury review, and what is the grand jury's responsibility?
   A. A serious civil case, and the grand jury will decide if there is a likelihood of conviction.
   B. A criminal case of terrorism against the people, and the grand jury will decide the guilt or innocence of the defendant.
   C. A criminal case, and the grand jury will determine the credibility of all witnesses.
   D. A criminal case, and the grand jury will decide whether to indict the defendant.

7. It happens after the first hearing, but it is not public. There is no jury, but the accused may have an attorney. After this hearing, the judge makes a decision, and in the next hearing, the judge decides the sentence. Which step in the juvenile court procedure has just been described?
   A. the initial hearing
   B. the adjudicatory hearing
   C. the adjunct hearing
   D. the dispositional hearing

8. Under criminal law, why is there not a single penalty for each crime?
   A. Crimes have a maximum and minimum penalty, which allows people guilty of the same crime to receive different punishments depending on the case.
   B. No two crimes are the same, and judges would not be able to keep track of all punishments.
   C. The prosecuting attorney gets to decide what the appropriate penalty is in each case.
   D. In criminal cases, juries are granted the final say in all laws and penalties.

9. What is "common law"?
   A. a set of legal codes
   B. local ordinances
   C. earlier court decisions
   D. statutes created by the legislature

10. During the discovery phase of a lawsuit, the plaintiff's attorney learns that a ten-year-old boy witnessed the auto accident that is the cause of the suit. What must the plaintiff's attorney do with this new evidence?
    A. use the boy as a surprise witness
    B. tell the defense about the witness
    C. file a civil lawsuit complaint
    D. call for a mistrial

11. When Brandon's band recorded its first CD, he made sure it carried a © symbol. What does this symbol mean?
    A. The content of the CD is considered property and protected by law.
    B. The band members named in the CD title are registered recording artists.
    C. The CD may be released on the Internet.
    D. The price of the CD is clearly marked on the bar code beneath the symbol.

12. Which is NOT a reason why a civil lawsuit can take nearly a year to settle?
    A. There are not enough people to serve on juries.
    B. It takes a long time to gather evidence.
    C. Lawyers can petition the courts to delay trials.
    D. There are not enough judges to handle the cases.

13. **Which type of crime was the 1995 bombing of a federal office building in Oklahoma City?**

    A. embezzlement

    B. racketeering

    C. terrorism

    D. larceny

14. **The airport near Rachel's new home recently added a runway. Now planes take off and land at all hours of the night. Rachel's family and the neighbors are furious. What might a court do to remedy the problem?**

    A. settle their case with equity by issuing an injunction

    B. pay for damages to their property

    C. file an injunction against the airport and receive compensation

    D. find the airport guilty of violating the Uniform Commercial Code

15. **Breaking a law in a nonviolent way because it goes against personal beliefs about what is right and wrong is known as**

    A. permissive courts.

    B. promoting the common good.

    C. white-collar crime.

    D. civil disobedience.

16. **A person who is convicted of embezzlement has**

    A. placed someone in fear of physical violence.

    B. stolen money that was entrusted into his or her care.

    C. betrayed the United States by helping its enemies.

    D. violated civil law but not criminal law.

17. **Which of the following is the first step by which an individual enters the criminal justice system?**

    A. parole

    B. bail

    C. arrest

    D. arraignment

18. **Rules that are enforced by governments are called**

    A. morals.

    B. laws.

    C. trusts.

    D. probable causes.

19. **The basic laws by which the United States government and the state governments are run are**

    A. common laws.

    B. bills of rights.

    C. civil cases.

    D. constitutions.

20. **What is the process by which an inmate goes free to serve the rest of his or her sentence outside of prison?**

    A. parole

    B. arraignment

    C. victimless crime

    D. plea bargaining

Benchmark Tests

Test 6

Directions: *Each question is followed by four choices. Identify the letter of the choice that best completes the statement or answers the question.*

1. Jeb is frustrated because voting day is next Tuesday, but he does not know anything about any of the candidates. What is the most important thing Jeb can do to become a better-informed voter?
   A. vote for the candidates who have been endorsed by the local newspaper
   B. contact the League of Women Voters for information on the candidates
   C. call his voting precinct and ask what type of ballot will be used
   D. register to vote at his local library

2. Which United Nations bureaucracy handles its daily tasks, translates documents, prepares reports, and provides services to UN councils and agencies?
   A. Secretariat
   B. Economic and Social Council
   C. General Assembly
   D. Amnesty International

3. "I am a farmer, a working man, and I do not want to see what happened in England happen here. There, the king has too much control, and the people are slaves to his wishes. In America, we need strong states' rights to support the will of the working man. I would oppose any type of strong national government!" To what party would this 1800s farmer probably belong?
   A. Federalist
   B. Socialist
   C. Republican
   D. Democratic-Republican

4. Which is NOT a defining characteristic of a nation?
   A. It has a territory set by borders.
   B. It has a diverse population.
   C. It has sovereignty.
   D. It has a government.

5. Why has the United Nations achieved its biggest successes when dealing with economic, rather than political, problems?
   A. Countries are most willing to work together when it does not mean giving up power.
   B. Most of the United Nations' members are economically stable nations.
   C. The economy, rather than politics, is the focus of United Nations' missions worldwide.
   D. Most nations have little interest in the politics of other nations.

6. What is "intelligence gathering"?
   A. seeking information about another country and what its government plans to do
   B. using an application process to determine who will work for the CIA
   C. persuading the most talented people from college campuses to work for the CIA
   D. strengthening governments that are friendly to the United States

7. **Mrs. Rogers lives in Switzerland with her family. She works as a consul and helps carry out America's foreign policy. What agency employs Mrs. Rogers?**
   A. the FBI
   B. the Department of State
   C. the Department of the Treasury
   D. the Department of Commerce

8. **How is the political party system similar to the system of checks and balances described in the Constitution?**
   A. Political parties have overlapping responsibilities.
   B. Political parties play a watchdog role, making sure other parties act responsibly.
   C. Each political party must have a balanced platform.
   D. Political parties must make sure that they present their ideas in a balanced way.

9. **What is it called when one country imports more than it exports?**
   A. interdependent trade
   B. command economy
   C. trade deficit
   D. trade surplus

10. **Look at the map of electoral votes by state. Why does the number of electoral votes per state change periodically?**
    A. The number of electoral votes is based on the changing number of registered voters in each state.
    B. An annual lottery is held to determine the number of electoral votes each state is awarded.
    C. Each state's actual voter turnout determines the number of electoral votes it receives.
    D. A change in population determined by the census affects the number of electoral votes each state has.

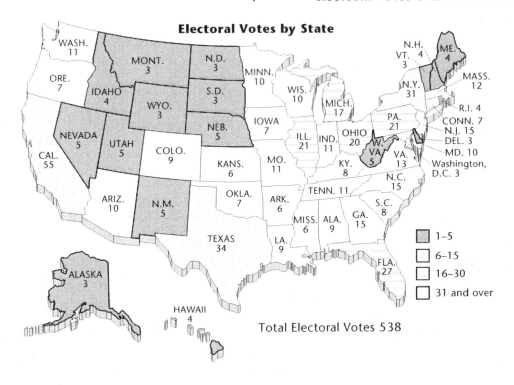

Electoral Votes by State

Total Electoral Votes 538

Name_____ Class_____ Date _____

11. What kind of propaganda technique is a candidate using when he or she discusses only those facts that support his or her argument?
    A. card stacking
    B. name calling
    C. bandwagon
    D. transfer

12. The EU, ASEAN, OAS, OAU, and NAFTA are all examples of what?
    A. trade organizations
    B. military alliances
    C. environmental alliances
    D. liberation organizations

13. If you were running for President, how could you receive money from the federal government to help support your campaign?
    A. raise at least $5,000 in each of 20 states
    B. be chosen as a political party candidate
    C. win the support of the delegates at the national convention
    D. pay election campaign taxes

14. What is one goal of American foreign policy?
    A. limiting democracy
    B. promoting world peace
    C. decreasing trade
    D. raising income taxes

15. Why should people in Canada be concerned about coal and oil production in the United States?
    A. Waste products from coal and oil production can be brought illegally into Canada through Canada's complex system of waterways.
    B. Acid rain, in the form of polluted fog, rain, and snow, can be caused by pollutants blown by the wind from the United States to Canada.
    C. Toxic chemicals formed from coal and oil may seep into the topsoil near the U.S.-Canadian border.
    D. The United States plans to export its coal and oil to Canadian industries, charging excessive fees.

16. When President Nixon traveled to China to meet with Chinese leaders, he was practicing
    A. multilateralism.
    B. foreign campaigning.
    C. democracy.
    D. diplomacy.

17. Historically, how have third-party candidates changed the outcomes of elections?
    A. They threw their support to one of the major party candidates on election day.
    B. They drew votes away from one of the major party candidates.
    C. Their supporters refused to vote for any candidate.
    D. Their supporters may have voted twice, making election results invalid.

"AND THEY WONDER WHY WE DON'T VOTE...."

18. **In this cartoon, what does the comment made by the woman watching television mean?**

   A. People do not vote because television ads are too loud.

   B. People do not vote because the polling places are not open long enough.

   C. People do not vote because they prefer to watch television.

   D. People do not vote because campaign ads focus too much on negative advertising.

19. **What diplomatic word or phrase is best described by these terms: lessening of tensions, treaties to slow arms race, distrust between nations eroded, and Intermediate-Range Nuclear Forces treaty?**

   A. savant

   B. Cold War

   C. détente

   D. renaissance

20. **Why did the 2000 presidential election lead to a debate over the various kinds of voting methods?**

   A. All nationwide balloting was done using the punch-card method, which has proved to be highly inaccurate.

   B. Some people thought their ballots were confusing and that they may not have voted for the candidate they intended.

   C. George W. Bush was elected by a landslide; therefore, many thought the voting process had been rigged.

   D. Third-party candidates received proportionally higher votes than anticipated.

Name_____ Class_____ Date _____

Report sheet:

Benchmark Test 1 _____ Overall Score_____

Question	Chapter/Section	Standard	Needs Review	Reading and Vocabulary Study Guide pages	Completed
1.	1.2	CG II.B		11–13	
2.	3.1	CG V.A		31–33	
3.	3.2	CG V.C		34–36	
4.	2.2	CG II.B		21–23	
5.	1.1	CG II.B		8–10	
6.	2.1	CG II.B		18–20	
7.	2.2	CG II.D		21–23	
8.	3.2	CG V.B		34–36	
9.	3.3	CG III.E		37–39	
10.	3.2	CG V.C		34–36	
11.	1.1	CG II.B		8–10	
12.	2.4	CG IV.A		27–29	
13.	1.1	CG II.B		8–10	
14.	3.2	CG V.E		34–36	
15.	2.4	CG I.D		27–29	
16.	2.4	CG I.A		27–29	
17.	2.4	CG I.A		27–29	
18.	3.2	CG V.C		34–36	
19.	2.3	CG II.B		24–26	
20.	2.4	CG I.D		27–29	

Parent Signature

_____

Name_____ Class_____ Date _____

Report sheet:

Benchmark Test 2 _____ Overall Score_____

Question	Chapter/Section	Standard	Needs Review	Reading and Vocabulary Study Guide pages	Completed
1.	5.3	CG III.A		57–59	
2.	6.3	CG V.B		67–69	
3.	5.3	CG III.A		57–59	
4.	6.3	CG II.D		67–69	
5.	7.2	CG III.D		74–76	
6.	4.1	CG II.C		41–43	
7.	5.1	CG III.B		51–53	
8.	7.1	CG V.B		71–73	
9.	6.2	CG II.B		64–66	
10.	7.2	CG V.B		74–76	
11.	5.2	CG II.D		54–56	
12.	6.1	CG III.D		61–63	
13.	4.3	CG I.A		47–49	
14.	7.1	CG III.D		71–73	
15.	4.1	CG IV.A		41–43	
16.	4.3	CG I.C		47–49	
17.	5.3	CG II.A		57–59	
18.	4.3	CG I.D		47–49	
19.	5.3	CG I.B		57–59	
20.	6.1	CG I.C		61–63	

Parent Signature

_____

Name_____ Class_____ Date_____

Report sheet:

Benchmark Test 3 _____ Overall Score_____

Question	Chapter/Section	Standard	Needs Review	Reading and Vocabulary Study Guide pages	Completed
1.	11.1	CG I.C		111–113	
2.	9.2	CG III.A		94–96	
3.	9.1	CG III.A		91–93	
4.	12.2	CG III.C		127–129	
5.	8.1	CG III.B		78–80	
6.	12.1	CG III.A		124–126	
7.	9.1	CG III.A		91–93	
8.	10.2	CG III.D		104–106	
9.	11.3	CG III.A		117–119	
10.	11.4	CG III.C		120–122	
11.	8.3	CG III.B		84–86	
12.	10.1	CG III.D		101–103	
13.	12.1	CG III.C		124–126	
14.	8.1	CG III.A		78–80	
15.	12.2	CG V.C		127–129	
16.	11.2	CG III.C		114–116	
17.	8.2	CG III.A		81–83	
18.	10.2	CG III.B		104–106	
19.	11.4	CG I.C		120–122	
20.	8.3	CG III.B		84–86	

Parent Signature

_____

Name_____ Class_____ Date _____

Report sheet:

Benchmark Test 4 _____ Overall Score_____

Question	Chapter/Section	Standard	Needs Review	Reading and Vocabulary Study Guide pages	Completed
1.	14.3	CG III.D		150–152	
2.	17.3	CG II.B		180–182	
3.	18.3	CG II.B		190–192	
4.	15.2	CG II.B		157–159	
5.	13.1	CG II.B		134–136	
6.	17.1	CG II.B		174–176	
7.	14.1	CG II.B		144–146	
8.	13.2	CG II.B		137–139	
9.	15.1	CG II.B		154–156	
10.	13.3	CG IV.A		140–142	
11.	16.2	CG II.B		167–169	
12.	13.3	CG IV.A		140–142	
13.	14.2	CG II.B		147–149	
14.	16.1	CG III.D		164–166	
15.	16.2	CG II.B		167–169	
16.	16.3	CG III.B		170–172	
17.	17.3	CG III.B		180–182	
18.	16.3	CG III.B		170–172	
19.	16.1	CG II.D		164–166	
20.	14.3	CG II.B		150–152	

Parent Signature

_____

Name_____ Class_____ Date _____

Report sheet:

Benchmark Test 5 _____ Overall Score_____

Question	Chapter/Section	Standard	Needs Review	Reading and Vocabulary Study Guide pages	Completed
1.	20.2	CG III.D		207–209	
2.	21.1	CG III.D		214–216	
3.	19.1	CG V.D		194–196	
4.	20.3	CG III.D		210–212	
5.	19.3	CG III.D		200–202	
6.	20.2	CG III.D		207–209	
7.	20.3	CG III.D		210–212	
8.	19.3	CG III.D		200–202	
9.	19.2	CG III.D		197–199	
10.	21.2	CG III.D		217–219	
11.	19.1	CG III.D		194–196	
12.	21.2	CG III.D		217–219	
13.	20.1	CG III.D		204–206	
14.	21.1	CG V.B		214–216	
15.	19.1	CG II.D		194–196	
16.	20.1	CG III.D		204–206	
17.	20.2	CG III.D		207–209	
18.	19.1	CG III.D		194–196	
19.	19.2	CG I.C		197–199	
20.	20.2	CG III.D		207–209	

Parent Signature

_____

Name_____ Class_____ Date _____

Report sheet:

Benchmark Test 6 _____ Overall Score_____

Question	Chapter/Section	Standard	Needs Review	Reading and Vocabulary Study Guide pages	Completed
1.	23.1	CG V.E		234–236	
2.	25.3	CG IV.A		260–262	
3.	22.2	CG II.D		227–229	
4.	25.1	CG IV.A		254–256	
5.	25.3	CG IV.A		260–262	
6.	24.1	CG IV.C		244–246	
7.	24.2	CG IV.B		247–249	
8.	22.1	CG II.C		224–226	
9.	24.2	CG IV.C		247–249	
10.	23.3	CG II.C		240–242	
11.	23.2	CG II.C		237–239	
12.	25.2	CG IV.C		257–259	
13.	22.3	CG III.E		230–232	
14.	24.1	CG IV.B		244–246	
15.	25.2	CG IV.B		257–259	
16.	24.1	CG IV.B		244–246	
17.	22.2	CG II.C		227–229	
18.	23.2	CG II.C		237–239	
19.	24.3	CG IV.B		250–252	
20.	23.1	CG II.C		234–236	

Parent Signature

_____

Name_____ Class_____ Date_____

Directions: *Each question is followed by four choices. Identify the letter of the choice that best completes the statement or answers the question.*

1. **In local government, what is the difference between a weak-mayor plan and a strong-mayor plan?**
   A. In a weak-mayor plan, the mayor hires a city manager to handle day-to-day business, but in a strong-mayor plan, the mayor appoints a council to handle day-to-day business.
   B. In a weak-mayor plan, the mayor appoints several commissioners to make ordinances, but in a strong-mayor plan, the commissioners are elected by voters.
   C. In a weak-mayor plan, the mayor does not have special executive powers, but in a strong-mayor plan, the mayor is in charge of the budget, making policies, and choosing city officials.
   D. In a weak-mayor plan, the mayor makes ordinances and decides how money should be spent, but in a strong-mayor plan, the mayor delegates these duties to his council.

2. **When President Thomas Jefferson acted without Congress's approval in buying the Louisiana Territory, what presidential power was he exercising?**
   A. the power to take private property
   B. the power of executive privilege
   C. the power to make treaties
   D. the power to purchase land from Native Americans

3. **What happened during World War II that brought the United States' isolationist foreign policy to an end?**
   A. German aggression caused Congress to declare war.
   B. The Arms Limitations Treaty was signed.
   C. American leaders met with Soviet leaders to make a peace plan.
   D. The Japanese bombed Pearl Harbor, bringing the United States into war.

4. **What determines the number of electors a state has in the Electoral College?**
   A. States have one elector for every 10,000 people.
   B. States have as many electors as they have members in the House of Representatives.
   C. States have one elector for every 100,000 people.
   D. States have as many electors as they have members of Congress.

5. **Which of the following is a reason someone in favor of free enterprise might argue against mandated recycling programs?**
   A. The government should not be able to dictate how much and what kind of packaging products should have.
   B. It is unconstitutional for the government to tax businesses.
   C. Companies should not be allowed to raise costs on products that are not recyclable.
   D. Congress should be able to pass laws that make businesses develop disposable goods.

6. **All of the following are determined by a state executive agency *except***
   A. the number of school days in a year.
   B. the subjects students must study.
   C. what books are appropriate for school libraries.
   D. educational requirements for teachers.

7. **Which region has experienced the greatest total population growth in the last several decades?**
   A. the Northwest
   B. the Sunbelt
   C. the Southwest
   D. the Rustbelt

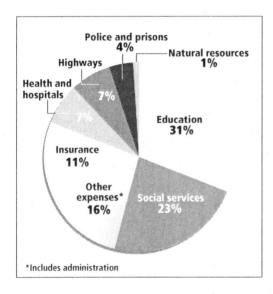

8. **The circle graph shows the government-funded services that are paid for by taxes and federal funds. Which service receives the largest percentage of state dollars?**
   A. social services
   B. education
   C. police and prisons
   D. other expenses

9. **Tara's mother would like to start a day-care center in her home. However, she learned that a local law prohibits her from using her home as a business. What type of law is this?**
   A. zoning
   B. public safety
   C. housing
   D. land revenue

10. **To become a member of the Democratic Party, you need to**
   A. declare your membership at a city council meeting.
   B. pay dues each year.
   C. think of yourself as a member.
   D. attend at least one meeting of the party.

11. **Which of these is an example of a public problem?**
   A. James missed the school bus.
   B. The traffic signal at a busy intersection is broken.
   C. Andrea has to pay a late fine to the public library.
   D. The mayor lost his bid for reelection.

Name_____ Class_____ Date _____

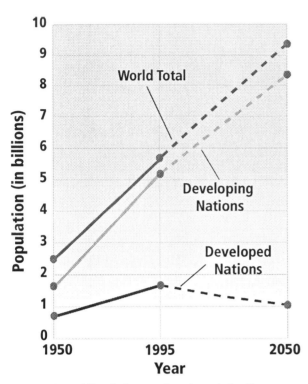

Dotted lines indicate projected population figures.

Source: United Nations Population Division

12. **Study the graph of world population. What is the projected total world population for the year 2050?**
   A. less than 9 billion
   B. more than 9 million
   C. more than 9 billion
   D. 1 billion

13. **What was the nation's first constitution after the Revolutionary War?**
   A. the Magna Carta
   B. the Articles of Confederation
   C. the Declaration of Independence
   D. the Bill of Rights

14. **A territory ruled by a more powerful nation is a**
   A. colony.
   B. sovereign nation.
   C. republic.
   D. developing nation.

15. **Which amendment protects someone from being forced to incriminate him or herself?**
   A. the First Amendment
   B. the Second Amendment
   C. the Fifth Amendment
   D. the Eighth Amendment

16. **Who has the power to declare a law unconstitutional?**
   A. the President
   B. the Attorney General
   C. the Senate
   D. the Supreme Court

17. **Which of the following is NOT a power of the President?**
   A. carry out laws and policies
   B. confirm nominations to the Supreme Court
   C. make treaties with other countries
   D. veto legislation

18. **In some states, the initiative, referendum, and recall give lawmaking powers to**
   A. governors.
   B. counties.
   C. citizens.
   D. judges.

19. **Powers shared by the federal and state governments are**
   A. concurrent powers.
   B. checks and balances.
   C. reserved powers.
   D. double jeopardy.

20. **An economy in which the government or a central authority controls the factors of production and makes key economic decisions is**
   A. a barter system.
   B. a market economy.
   C. mercantilism.
   D. a command economy.

21. **Which form of city government was created as a response to corrupt politics in the early 1900s?**

    A. the home rule plan

    B. the council-manager plan

    C. the system of checks and balances

    D. the weak-mayor plan

22. **Which of the following is NOT a source of revenue for the federal government?**

    A. income tax

    B. sales tax

    C. tariffs

    D. sales of government-owned resources

23. **Who oversees the executive branch of a state government?**

    A. the U.S. State Department

    B. the state senators

    C. the governor

    D. the lieutenant governor

24. **What is the area that a U.S. Senator represents?**

    A. a state

    B. a congressional district

    C. an interest group

    D. an executive department

25. **Formal agreements between nations are called**

    A. executive privileges.

    B. national conventions.

    C. foreign policies.

    D. treaties.

Essay

Directions: *On a separate sheet of paper, write a short essay of two or three paragraphs to answer each of the questions.*

26. **U.S. Supreme Court cases have dealt with a variety of important issues that have affected American society. Select two Supreme Court cases from the list below. Explain the Court's decision in each case and discuss the impact of each decision on American society.**

    Marbury v. *Madison* (1803) — judicial review

    Brown v. *Board of Education of Topeka* (1954) — equal protection under the law

    Miranda v. *Arizona* (1966) — rights of the accused

    Tinker v. *Des Moines School District* (1969) — free speech

27. **Since it was written in 1787, the Constitution has provided the nation with a plan for government. However, a number of major changes have been made to the Constitution over the years. Using your knowledge of U.S. history and government, write an essay in which you discuss how the Constitution was both (a) a product of its time, and (b) a document that has had enough flexibility to meet the challenges of the future.**

Answer Key

Middle Grades Test 1

1. A
2. A
3. D
4. C
5. D
6. B

Middle Grades Test 2

7. B
8. C
9. D
10. D
11. D
12. D
13. C
14. C

Middle Grades Test 3

15. C
16. C
17. A
18. B
19. B
20. B
21. A
22. A
23. B
24. C

High School Test 1

1. D
2. C
3. B
4. A
5. D
6. B

High School Test 2

7. C
8. D
9. A
10. A
11. A

High School Test 3

12. A
13. C
14. D
15. B
16. C
17. B

Diagnosing Readiness Tests

Middle Grades Test 1— Geographic Literacy

1. C
2. B
3. A
4. C
5. B
6. C
7. A
8. C
9. C
10. A
11. C
12. A
13. B
14. B
15. D
16. C
17. A

Middle Grades Test 2—Visual Analysis

1. B
2. C
3. C
4. D
5. C
6. C
7. D
8. C
9. A
10. D

Middle Grades Test 3— Critical Thinking and Reading

1. B
2. A
3. D
4. B
5. C
6. B
7. C
8. C
9. C
10. A
11. A
12. D
13. C
14. A
15. C
16. B

Middle Grades Test 4— Communications

1. D
2. A
3. B
4. C
5. C
6. B
7. D
8. D
9. C
10. B
11. B
12. D
13. D
14. C
15. D
16. B
17. B
18. C
19. A
20. A

Middle Grades Test 5— Vocabulary

1. B
2. D
3. B
4. A
5. B
6. A
7. B
8. C
9. B
10. B
11. D
12. C
13. B
14. D
15. D
16. B

Middle Grades Test 6— Writing

p. 36
Students' answers will vary, but should express an opinion on the issue as the main idea and support the main idea with related reasons.

p. 37
Students' paragraphs will vary, but should clearly outline the similarities and differences between two potential pets.

p. 38
Example main idea summary:
Take Our Daughters and Sons to Work Day gives young people a chance to accompany their parents to the workplace, providing several positive benefits.

p. 39
Sample Answer:

Title: How to Prepare in Case of a Fire

I. Create an emergency escape plan
   A. How to get out of the house
      1. Identify two exits from every room
   B. Location to meet away from the house

II. Points to Remember in Case of a Fire
   A. Do not try to put out the fire
   B. Alert everyone to the fire
   C. Leave immediately and do not go back inside
   D. Call 911 from a neighbor's house
   E. Stop, drop, and roll if clothes on fire
   F. Stay low in case of smoke

III. Other preventative measures
   A. Hold a fire drill once or twice a year
   B. Smoke detectors
      1. Make sure everyone recognizes the sound of a smoke detector
      2. Check smoke detectors once a month
      3. Change batteries once or twice a year

High School Test 1— Geographic Literacy

1. A
2. D
3. C
4. B
5. B
6. D
7. A
8. B
9. A
10. B
11. B
12. B
13. C
14. A
15. B
16. D
17. D
18. B

High School Test 2—Visual Analysis

1. C
2. B
3. A
4. D
5. C
6. A
7. C

High School Test 3—Critical Thinking and Reading

1. C
2. B
3. D
4. C
5. A
6. D
7. C
8. B
9. A
10. C
11. B
12. D
13. A
14. C
15. A
16. D

High School Test 4— Communications

1. B
2. D
3. C
4. B
5. C
6. A
7. D

8. B
9. C
10. B
11. D
12. A
13. C
14. D

High School Test 5— Vocabulary

1. B
2. A
3. C
4. D
5. C
6. D
7. A
8. B
9. C
10. A
11. D
12. B
13. A
14. D
15. D
16. B

High School Test 6—Writing

p. 59
Students' outlines will vary, but should follow the basic outline format provided. They should express an opinion on this issue, and use the major headings, subheads, and supporting details to illustrate and support their position.

p. 60
Student responses will vary, but should summarize the passage and show a clear understanding of the main idea.

Example: Although people participate in ecotourism with the hope of improving local economies and preserving wild places, irresponsible ecotourism can have harmful effects. Travelers should research how to practice tourism that is truly environmentally friendly.

Diagnosing Readiness Tests *continued*

p. 61
Students' paragraphs will vary, but should focus on a topic that involves two or more causative factors leading to an effect. Paragraphs should clearly explain how the causes contributed to the effect.

p. 62
Students' letters will vary, but should clearly express a position and cite details to support their position.

Benchmark Tests

Test 1
1. B
2. D
3. B
4. D
5. D
6. A
7. C
8. B
9. B
10. D
11. C
12. B
13. D
14. A
15. A
16. D
17. B
18. C
19. B
20. C

Test 2
1. D
2. B
3. C
4. D
5. D
6. D
7. C
8. C
9. A
10. A
11. B
12. A
13. C
14. C
15. A
16. D
17. A
18. A
19. A
20. B

Test 3
1. C
2. C
3. D
4. B
5. B
6. B
7. C
8. A
9. A
10. B
11. A
12. B
13. D
14. B
15. B
16. B
17. C
18. D
19. C
20. D

Test 4
1. A
2. C
3. A
4. B
5. B
6. D
7. C
8. B
9. C
10. A
11. D
12. D
13. D
14. B
15. A
16. D
17. A
18. B
19. C
20. A

Test 5
1. B
2. A
3. A
4. D
5. A
6. D
7. B
8. A
9. C
10. B
11. A
12. A
13. C
14. A
15. D
16. B
17. C
18. B
19. D
20. A

Test 6
1. B
2. A
3. D
4. B
5. A
6. A
7. B
8. B
9. C
10. D
11. A
12. A
13. A
14. B
15. B
16. D
17. B
18. D
19. C
20. B

Outcome Test

1. C
2. C
3. D
4. D
5. A
6. C
7. B
8. B
9. A
10. C
11. B
12. C
13. B
14. A
15. C
16. D
17. B
18. C
19. A
20. D
21. B
22. B
23. C
24. A
25. D

Essays

26. Students should describe any two cases. Examples:
Marbury v. *Madison* (1803): William Marbury sued Secretary of State James Madison because he did not get a government job. The Supreme Court's decision in this case had a much wider effect. It established a precedent that gave the Court the power of judicial review, or the power to overturn any law that violates the U.S. Constitution.

Brown v. *Board of Education of Topeka* (1954): Because an African American girl was not allowed to attend a school for white children, her parents took the school board to court. The Supreme Court ruled that "separate but equal" schools could never really be equal.

Therefore, segregated educational facilities violated the principle of equal protection and were unconstitutional. This ruling led to the overturning of all segregation laws.

Miranda v. *Arizona* (1966): The Supreme Court ruled that when a person is arrested, police must inform him or her of the constitutional rights to remain silent and to have the advice of a lawyer.

Tinker v. *Des Moines School District* (1969): Students who wore black armbands to school to protest the Vietnam War were suspended. The Supreme Court ruled that the armbands were a form of "speech" because they represented ideas. Also, the Court stated that students do have a basic right to free speech.

27. Students' essays will vary, but should mention (a) elements of the Constitution as originally written, including the lack of a bill of rights, the absence of protections for African Americans, and the unequal position of women. Students should also recognize (b) that the writers deliberately specified a way for the Constitution to be amended, allowing it to adapt to different ideas and morals as times changed. Among the most important amendments have been the Bill of Rights; the 13th, 14th, and 15th Amendments, which banned slavery and protected the rights of African Americans; and the 19th Amendment, which guaranteed the right of women to vote.

Acknowledgments

Text credits: pg. 5, "Papa's Parrot" from *Every Living Thing* by Cynthia Rylant. Text copyright © 1985 by Cynthia Rylant. Reprinted with permission of Atheneum Books for Young Readers, an imprint of Simon & Schuster Children's Publishing Division. pg. 7, from *Wildlife at Risk: Pandas* by Gillian Standring. Copyright © 1991 by Wayland (Publishers) Ltd. pg. 9, from *Into Thin Air: A Personal Account of the Mount Everest Disaster* by Jon Krakauer. Copyright © 1997 by Jon Krakauer. pgs. 11–12, "In Patagonia." Reprinted and edited with the permission of Simon & Schuster Adult Publishing Group, from *In Patagonia* by Bruce Chatwin. Copyright © 1977 by Bruce Chatwin. All Rights Reserved. pg. 13–14, from "Joy, Luck and Hollywood" from the *Los Angeles Times* by Amy Tan. Copyright © 1993 by Amy Tan. pg. 24, "The Envious Buffalo" from *The Fables of India.* Copyright © 1955 by Joseph Gaer. Used by permission. pg. 26, "The Eternal Frontier" from *Frontier* by Louis L'Amour. Copyright © by Louis L'Amour Enterprises, Inc. pg. 53, *All Quiet on the Western Front* by Erich Maria Remarque. *Im Westen Nichts Neues,* Copyright © 1928 by Ullstein A.G.; Copyright renewed © 1956 by Erich Maria Remarque. *All Quiet on the Western Front,* Copyright © 1929, 1930 by Little, Brown and Company; Copyright renewed © 1957, 1958 by Erich Maria Remarque. All Rights Reserved.

Art credits: pg. 22, Gary Brookins; pg. 44, (both) National Archives and Records Administration; pg. 79, Tribune Media Services; pg. 81, Chris Britt; pg. 85, The Granger Collection; pg. 93, John Trever

Note: Every effort has been made to locate the copyright owners of material reprinted in this book. Omissions brought to our attention will be corrected in subsequent editions.